Economic Costs of Air Pollution

PRAEGER SPECIAL STUDIES IN
U.S. ECONOMIC AND SOCIAL DEVELOPMENT

Economic Costs of Air Pollution

STUDIES IN MEASUREMENT

Ronald G. Ridker

FREDERICK A. PRAEGER, Publishers
New York · Washington · London

1967

The purpose of the Praeger Special Studies is to make specialized research monographs in U.S. and international economics and politics available to the academic, business, and government communities. For further information, write to the Special Projects Division, Frederick A. Praeger, Publishers, 111 Fourth Avenue, New York, N.Y. 10003.

FREDERICK A. PRAEGER, PUBLISHERS
111 Fourth Avenue, New York, N.Y. 10003, U.S.A.
77-79 Charlotte Street, London W.1, England

Published in the United States of America in 1967
by Frederick A. Praeger, Inc., Publishers

Library of Congress Catalog Card Number: 66-26571

Printed in the United States of America

ACKNOWLEDGMENTS

While many persons were involved in the work reflected in this book, several who were singularly important in different chapters deserve prominent mention.

Dr. Alphonse Holtmann, Wayne State University, is the author of the unit cost estimates for various diseases presented in Chapter 3, "Economic Costs of Diseases Associated with Air Pollution." He deserves special recognition for his contribution to this chapter.

The household survey presented in the second half of Chapter 4 was developed, implemented, and analyzed, on the basis of general specifications provided, by Daniel Yankelovich, Inc. of Philadelphia. Dr. Donald Streever, Dr. Warren Wittreich, and Mrs. Jane O'Donnell were principally involved in this effort. Dr. Marnie Mueller, formerly of Washington University, St. Louis, developed many of the materials for the first half of this chapter. She served as a research associate during the first year of this project. Her principal contribution to this project is reflected in a study not included in this book but available through the Division of Air Pollution, U.S. Public Health Service, entitled "A Projection of Air Pollution Problems in St. Louis."

The contribution of William D. Watson, currently at the University of Minnesota, was especially important in the development of Chapter 5, "A Case Study of a Pollution Episode." In addition, he served as a responsible, efficient, and tireless research assistant throughout the second year of this project. I was most fortunate to have had his aid.

Dr. John Henning, Syracuse University, is principally responsible for many sections of Chapter 6, "Property Values and Air Pollution: A Cross-Section Study of One City." In addition, he helped in revising Chapter 7 and saw us all through the exasperating experience of talking to a computer.

While Dr. Hugh Nourse, University of Illinois, and I are jointly responsible for the second of the property value studies, presented in Chapter 7, he had the critical and painstaking task of gathering the data and undertaking the preliminary computations. Dr. Nourse also assisted in the development and preliminary analysis of materials for Chapter 5. His knowledge of the St. Louis area generally and its real estate market in particular proved to be a great asset in these as well as other chapters involving St. Louis.

Lauri Zeh typed the penultimate draft of this manuscript. Charles Lerner, who served as editor, is responsible for turning a very rough work into a finished product; Marian Jones typed the final version for photocopying. I am especially grateful to them for their time, care, and concern.

The contributions of others are more difficult to specify in detail. Certainly the most important is that of Lester Goldner of the Division of Air Pollution of the U.S. Public Health Service. Officially, he served as project officer in monitoring the contracts between the Public Health Service and Washington and Syracuse Universities which supported this work. (In addition, partial support for computer services was provided by the National Science Foundation.) But his unofficial contribution -- in providing background, contacts, and above all encouragement beyond the call of duty during some of the darker periods -- was far more important. The help of Ivars Gutmanis and William Skwersky, of his office, should also be acknowledged.

Other persons of the Division of Air Pollution who provided important data and comments are almost too numerous to mention. In the Technical Assistance Branch, James D. Williams, Jack W. Sadler, Ronald A. Venezia, Jack Farmer, and Norman Edminsten were especially important. Emanual Landau, Robert J. M. Horton, Roy O. McCaldin, James B. Upham, Charles R. Sharp, Roman K. Hofman, John H. Ludwig, Bernard Steigerwald, and Frederick A. Rohrman must also be thanked.

The penultimate draft of the manuscript was read by Allen Kneese, William Vickrey, Mason Gaffney, Thomas Crocker, and Robert Strotz, all of whom provided very useful comments. Needless to say, none of them, nor any of those mentioned above, is responsible for errors in the final product.

Portions of Chapter 2 appeared in The Economics of Air Pollution, edited by Harold Wolozin and published by W.W. Norton; and Chapter 6 is a revised version of an article by John Henning and me appearing in the Review of Economics and Statistics. I wish to thank the editors of these publications for permission to use these materials here. Finally, I want to thank Carol, Anne, and Paul for bearing with me during the evenings and weekends devoted to this manuscript rather than to them.

Ronald G. Ridker
Washington, D.C.

CONTENTS

LIST OF TABLES

xi

LIST OF FIGURES

CHAPTER 1 INTRODUCTION:
STANDARD-SETTING
AS A FRAME OF
REFERENCE

Economists have long recognized the need for public regulation of economic activities that result in unwanted side
effects. These effects -- called "external diseconomies" in
the language of economics -- may arise whenever market
forces alone are insufficient to make an individual bear all
the costs resulting from his actions. Air pollution, which
results from using air as a waste-disposal medium, is an ex-
cellent example of an external diseconomy, since there are
clearly no market forces that compel the user to consider the
costs he imposes on others. Without regulation, therefore,
the air is used as if no such costs were present and air pollution rises to a level that is socially undesirable.

But despite their long-standing recognition of air pollution
as a ubiquitous example of these side effects, economists
have not undertaken studies that contribute significantly to
answering the hard questions facing policy-makers: For example, what level of pollution is socially acceptable? What
should be done to achieve this standard? How can costs be
allocated fairly to all those who contribute to air pollution?
What institutional arrangements will ensure effective use of
the limited answers we have for these questions? Although
such questions have been discussed increasingly in recent
years, there has been no attempt to produce useful operational
answers. For example, economists have recommended that
an effluent charge or tax be levied on emissions in order to
induce behavior that will lead to acceptable levels of air pollution. Of the various arguments made against this proposal,
the most telling is that no one has ventured to suggest what

1

the magnitude of such a charge should be or even how --
except at an abstract level -- to determine what it should be.

These operational questions have not been addressed because they require empirical information far beyond our
current understanding of the problem -- information that will
permit us to estimate the net social benefits (benefits minus
costs) that would result from a given change in controls on
emissions. But there are many causal links between controls
and net benefits, and we need quantitative information about
each link in order to specify the over-all relationship. We
need to know how pollutors are likely to respond to given
changes in controls, and the extent to which emission levels
will be affected by changes in their activities (which include
such ordinary and universal activities as producing goods,
traveling, and disposing of trash). We need to know how a
change in emission levels is likely to affect ambient air quality, a relationship that is strongly influenced by meteorological, topological, and climatic conditions. We need to know the
relationship between ambient air quality and direct loss,
a relationship obscured by the presence of many other, often
more important, factors that cause the same type of losses.
We need to know how individuals adjust to offset these losses.
Finally, we need to measure the resulting losses in common
terms so they can be added together and compared.

This list of requirements is not meant to suggest a council
of perfection. Even crude approximations would permit some
responsible judgments to be made. But the state of our knowledge is such that in many important cases even educated
guesses about the specific form of these relationships are
lacking.

In the face of these complex relationships, so inadequately
understood and even less fully quantified, progress is most
likely to be made by concentrating empirical efforts on fairly
small links in the whole causal chain. This study deals with
one of them: the relationship between ambient air quality and
economic loss; and more specifically with the development

and testing of methods for quantifying this relationship. To this end, three methods for measuring the economic consequences of air pollution are presented in Chapter 2 and applied in six case studies that follow. Several of these studies end with cost estimates, though it should be emphasized that the principal purpose of those estimates is to illustrate and test the methods. This is consistent with the stress in this study on methodological considerations rather than policy implications. With this emphasis, the study should be useful principally to the researcher who wishes to apply its methods in deriving specific estimates, but also to the policy-maker who cannot intelligently employ such estimates without understanding their limitations and underlying assumptions.

The scope of this study is further narrowed by a concentration on methods of measuring the economic consequences of normal levels of urban air pollution. The term "economic consequences," here defined broadly to include health, property, and aesthetic losses, excludes agricultural losses and -- with one partial exception -- unique pollution episodes and situations.

Finally, the results of this study are limited in that, while each major approach is applied in at least one illustrative case, it was not possible to apply them all to the problems of a single locality. This limitation results from gaps in available data and a budgetary restraint on the collection of new data, which made it necessary to select localities where data would provide adequate tests of each method. Unfortunately, this means that the numerical results derived from the respective methods cannot be compared with each other. It also means that this study cannot sketch a complete picture of the pollution costs in any one locality. Thus, while it provides estimates wherever possible, this study is essentially exploratory; it is meant to determine what can be done and what needs to be done to measure the economic costs of air pollution.

The difficulties in setting standards of ambient air quality are at the heart of most policy problems and raise all the measurement problems at issue in this study. Standard setting is therefore a useful context in which to present a frame of reference for describing the derived measurements.

Two lists would provide the raw material for a rational setting of air-pollution standards: in one, all the changes necessary to bring about a given alteration in air quality, and in the other all the consequences that result from this alteration. If the items in each list could be assigned realistic dollar values -- and we will assume for the moment that this is possible -- the lists would represent two broad categories of costs. The first will be called the "costs of control." Although the second is clearly a list of the "benefits of control," for the sake of a later discussion we will call it the "costs of pollution," since it represents the benefits foregone in the absence of controls. With rather grim humor, the first category could also be called the "benefits of pollution," for these are the costs that could be eliminated by permitting pollution to occur without regulation.

If costs for all the items in these lists can be estimated for each different level of pollution that is of interest for policy purposes, they could be conveniently represented as curves similar to those presented in Figure 1a. As the level of pollution rises above zero, the cost of pollution (curve CP) may remain at zero for a time, or appear to be zero because our measurements are not sensitive to the costs of very low pollution levels. But at some point t, the curve CP can be expected to begin rising and to continue rising at an increasing rate, eventually becoming vertical at extremely high concentrations where all life would cease. The cost of control (curve CC), on the other hand, is zero at point r, representing the level of pollution prevailing in the absence of controls. To reduce pollution below this point, costs must be increased. The CC curve eventually becomes vertical as it rises to the left, indicating that at those low levels of pollution all our

Figure 1
Total Costs, Sum of Total Costs, and Marginal Costs

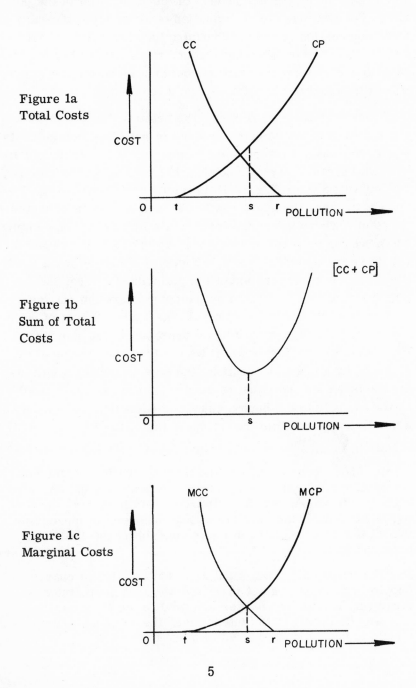

Figure 1a
Total Costs

Figure 1b
Sum of Total
Costs

Figure 1c
Marginal Costs

resources cannot further reduce the concentration of the pollutant. For example, the elimination of all pollutants resulting
from combustion is likely to require the elimination of all
combustion; and because background radiation is always present, our exposure to radiation could not be entirely eliminated
unless we lived in the equivalent of a lead box.

From a social point of view, the best level at which to set
the standard is where both the costs of pollution and the costs
of control, taken together, are minimum. Figures 1b and 1c
are two different ways of showing this point of minimum cost.
The curve shown in Figure 1b is the (vertical) sum of the CP
and CC curves, the appropriate standard obviously indicated
by point s where the curve reaches a minimum value. Figure
1c shows the marginal cost curves, each of which indicates
how the corresponding curve in Figure 1a changes for a small
change in the concentration of the pollutant. [1] Here, the appropriate standard is indicated by the point where the marginal
cost of control (curve MCC) equals the marginal cost of pollution (curve MCP). Point s again represents that standard. [2]
This equality indicates that, if we try to reduce the level of
pollution by a small decrement, the cost of control would increase by an amount equal to the cost of the damage caused
by the air pollution. Such a change is equivalent to moving
a small distance within the trough of the [CP + CC] curve of

----

[1]In other words, they are the first derivatives of the corresponding total curves with respect to a change in concentration of pollution except that, in order to present both curves
in the same quadrant, the minus sign has been dropped from
the MCC curve. Also to improve readability the scale has
been changed.

[2]Parenthetically, we might note that an effluent charge
should in principal be set in such a way that the pollutor is
faced with a scale of charges identical to the MCP curve. In
this way he is forced to "internalize" the costs he forces
others to bear and is induced to move to point s.

Figure 1b. We gain nothing by inducing a change at that point; either an increase or a decrease in pollution from that level would entail an economic loss to society.

If measurements are to be useful within this analytical framework, they should possess certain characteristics. First, and most important, they must tell us more than the current total costs of pollution and of control; knowing only where we currently are on the curves of Figure 1a could be misleading. Informed decisions require a knowledge of the current marginal costs of pollution and of control, that is, where we are on the curves of Figure 1c. Marginal costs will at least indicate the direction in which, if not the exact point toward which, policy should move. In particular, the fact that the total costs of pollution are greater than the costs of control does not, by itself, indicate that optimal standards are being violated and that therefore more should be spent on control.

This point must be emphasized because all too often one reads statements implying the contrary. In an article in the Saturday Review, C. W. Griffin, Jr., relying on commonly quoted figures, stated:

> Even if air pollution presented no human health
> hazard whatsoever, we could justify a tremendous
> strengthening of control on purely economic
> grounds...The nation's total bill is estimated at
> $11 billion a year, about twenty times the most op-
> timistic estimate of total national expenditures by
> industry and by all levels of government for con-
> trol devices, research and enforcement programs. [3]

This statement is obviously based on the unstated (and unsup-ported) assumption that when there is such a large discrepancy

---

[3]C. W. Griffin, Jr., "America's Airborne Garbage," Saturday Review, May 22, 1965, p. 34.

between the cost of pollution and the cost of control (assuming for the moment that the estimates are reasonably correct), an additional million dollars spent on controls will reduce the costs of pollution by at least that much. This of course is conceivable, but it is also conceivable that an additional million will result in less than that amount of improvement. For example, considering only Figure 1a, at the level of pollution (s) corresponding to the standard set in Figures 1b and 1c, the total cost of pollution is higher than the total cost of control.[4] Following the argument implicit in the quoted paragraph, a community would spend money to move its pollution level to the left until the total costs were equal. But this would have moved the pollution level away from the point of minimum combined costs of pollution and control; that is, it would have increased the combined costs to that community. Empirical evidence on the marginal costs is therefore necessary to support any program of pollution control.[5]

The total cost of pollution at a given time may be useful for other reasons. Policy-makers may not give proposals a hearing, or even authorize an investigation unless they are first shown that the problem involved is a serious one, relative to others they must consider. For this purpose total cost is likely to be more impressive than the excess of marginal benefits over marginal costs; and figures such as those quoted

---

[4]This is purely a function of the position in which the curves have been drawn. Obviously curve CP could be shifted vertically -- indeed, even shifted downward until CP is less than CC -- without affecting the position of point s in Figure 1b or 1c.

[5]In evaluating control programs that are expected to reduce the cost of a particular pollutant to zero, the total cost is the relevant marginal cost figure. The introduction of control equipment that will virtually eliminate the emission of fluorides from a specific plant is a case in point. But this is simply a special case of the general principle.

above undoubtedly helped achieve the passage of the Clean Air
Act of 1963. But once the proposal has obtained a hearing and
the issue becomes what to do about the problem, the total cost
figures are irrelevant. [6]

The second characteristic of useful measurements is that
they should be made within a specific air shed and on specific
pollutants (or groups of them if they act, or can be acted upon,
together). Each pollutant has its own characteristics and each
community faces different meteorological, topological,and
economic conditions. The appropriate standard, therefore,
will vary with the pollutant and the community being studied.
This point suggests that national estimates of pollution and
control costs are not useful for setting standards, even if they
could be made in marginal terms. As a first approximation
and a matter of convenience, we may wish to set some common
standards for the nation as a whole; but even so, local rather
than national data should be used for this purpose.

Third, the costs that are measured should be minimum
costs. With respect to the costs of control, it is self-evident
that the standard will not be set correctly unless each point on
the curve represents the minimum cost of achieving the implied reduction in pollution levels. But the same is also true
for costs of pollution. If it is cheaper for an asthma victim to
move from an area than to continue suffering, only the losses
he would incur in moving should be included in the cost of pollution curve. If this procedure is not followed, the standard
could easily be set too low, considering the interests of the
pollutor as well as those of the person who suffers from
pollution.

---

[6]There are great, perhaps insurmountable,difficulties
involved in estimating total costs. These are discussed in a
1966 report to the Division of Air Pollution entitled, The
Problem of Estimating Total Costs of Air Pollution, a Discussion and an Illustration, by the present author. These difficulties raise further doubts about the value of the published
estimates.

This point has more relevance for research into the costs of control than it does for this study, for we have little choice but to assume that the observed costs of pollution damage are the minimum costs we wish to measure. In the case of the asthma victim who stays in the polluted area, we must assume that he knows what he is doing, i.e., that for him it is cheaper to stay than to move (perhaps because of the psychic costs involved in moving).[7] While this is equivalent to assuming rational and knowledgeable behavior, any other assumption would require us to look into the mind of each affected person to determine whether he is properly adjusting to the pollution damages he faces, a task far beyond the scope of this (and very likely any other) study. But cases can arise in which the assumption is clearly unjustifiable, and we must be prepared to adjust the cost estimates to make them useful for standard setting purposes.

Finally, point s will represent the appropriate standard only if the CC and CP curves do in fact measure and aggregate all the benefits and costs adequately. Actually, of course, many important consequences cannot be measured, and the policy-maker must use his intuition and judgment to modify the answer obtained from the quantitative analysis. To aid in this process a qualitative analysis of nonquantifiable variables should be included; at the very least such an analysis will indicate the direction of the biases imposed by the special assumptions and omissions involved in the quantitative studies.

It should be recognized that measurements with these characteristics ignore dynamic elements -- the forces that tend to shift the CC and CP curves to the right or left. For example, the cost of pollution curve tends to shift to the right as activities giving rise to pollution and the number of objects subject to pollution damage grow over time, whereas the cost

_____

[7]We must also assume that he does not stay in order to influence the determination of standards.

of control curve will shift to the left whenever a technological breakthrough in the control of pollution occurs. A change in tastes can also affect the shape or position of these curves. At a minimum, this additional dimension to the problem of standard setting requires that the cost curves be recalculated periodically to adjust the standard to new circumstances. [8]

In conclusion, it is useful to refer to the criticism that has been leveled against this analytical framework, namely, that so small a portion of the relevant consequences can be quantified that the effort is not worth it. Three points can be made in reply. First, the organization and structuring of the problem in terms that are useful for measurement and the clarification of issues that typically result may be much more useful to the policy-maker than the measurements themselves. Second, a consequence of this study should be a better understanding of the specific types of data needed to make future measurements more valuable. Third, and most important, this question cannot be settled a priori: There is no way to know in advance of measurement whether or not a usefully large portion of the consequences of a proposed action can be quantified. Of course, all relevant consequences of an action are unlikely ever to become measurable. But we can hope to whittle down the area within which unsupported opinion and emotive rhetoric dominate.

---

[8]A more satisfactory procedure would be to set the standard after taking into account both the current and the expected future position of the cost and benefit schedules. A preliminary consideration of this problem and some estimates of the future air-pollution problem for one city can be found in A Projection of Air Pollution Problems in St. Louis, a 1966 report submitted by this author to the Division of Air Pollution, U.S. Public Health Service, and available from them.

CHAPTER 2 STRATEGIES FOR MEASURING THE COST OF AIR POLLUTION

This chapter develops and discusses three strategies of measurement that can be used to estimate the shape of the cost-of-pollution curves (described in Chapter 1) for given localities and specific types of pollutants. We wish to know the shape of such curves so that, in conjunction with similar information on the costs of control, appropriate standards and policies to enforce them can be specified. Also, in order to indicate the general magnitude of the problem, we would like to know where on such curves we are today and, if no changes in policy were instituted, where we are likely to be in the future.

Air pollution is a multidimensional phenomenon. Its sources are varied, it affects a multitude of objects, and it can produce wide variety of changes in behavior. Its effects are not always immediate; some tend to be spread over time in different ways depending on the object affected. To add to these problems, data are poor, the relevant functions are stochastic, and the "independent variables" of any given analysis are sometimes highly intercorrelated. In these circumstances it is unrealistic to try to identify a priori proxies to represent broad categories of pollutants or effects. Such useful indexes may exist, but they must be discovered through a series of studies on a fairly detailed, disaggregated level.

However, while we cannot simplify the problem through aggregation, we can make it more manageable with a number of assumptions. First, factors having the same consequences as air pollution, as well as our knowledge about ways to adjust to these consequences, are assumed to be constant. We thus ignore, for example, changes in nonpollution causes of diseases related to air pollution, as well as improvements in our ability to prevent diseases. This assumption is fairly realistic for different observations (within this country) at the same point in time; and since there are comparatively few time-series data available on air pollution, we must in any case rely upon cross-section data. Second, intervening variables such as topological and meteorological conditions are assumed to be constant. A corrosive pollutant, for example, will cause more damage in warm, humid weather than in a cold, dry climate. But such variables typically behave in irregular and unpredictable ways, and their effects on the consequences of air pollution are not fully understood. We can only take care to choose case studies in which such factors are, in fact, constant. This consideration casts some doubt on the usefulness of cross-section interurban studies, but does not affect intra-urban studies for at any one time within a city, weather conditions can be assumed to be more or less constant.

Third, we must assume that adequate air-pollution measurements are available and -- equally important -- that we know how to use them. That is, we must know enough about how pollution works to know what measures of central tendency and dispersion best represent the frequency, duration, and intensity of different pollution levels. These last assumptions are obviously unrealistic in many instances, but without them the search for measurements of the economic costs of pollution damage cannot proceed.

Finally, changes in air-pollution levels are assumed to have negligible effects on such economic variables as employment, income distribution, and production methods. If the level of air pollution were reduced, window washers, paint manufacturers and possibly even doctors would do less business; but the controls that brought about this reduction would stimulate employment in the manufacture of control devices. In effect, we assume that such shifts in employment occur relatively easily and that their net effect can be ignored.

Now consider a community in which ambient air quality as measured on a particular scale -- say, annual geometric mean sulfation rates[1] -- deteriorates. The effects of this deterioration can be grouped into three categories, each of which gives use to a different approach to measurement. First, there are certain direct and immediate effects. Pollution might damage paint, irritate the throat, discolor the leaves of plants, and raise certain age-specific mortality and morbidity rates. Second, these effects induce persons and firms to make certain adjustments in order to reduce the direct impact of the pollutant. An asthmatic might adjust by moving from the area, a spinach grower by shifting to another crop, and a homeowner by painting more often. These adjustments, which may reduce the cost of the direct effects of the increased pollution, can be quite costly in their own right. Third, these adjustments involve actions that affect others. When spinach growers move, the price of spinach is likely to be affected and some jobs will be created while others are eliminated. Such social interactions can be quite important consequences of the initial rise in pollution.

---

[1]For a definition of sulfation rates see p. 207 under the section entitled SUL, plus the reference cited therein.

In most of the measurement studies the geometric mean is used, the reasons being that it is readily available, in common use by pollution experts, and that many distributions of observations on pollution appear log-normal. However, it is a measure that gives little weight to large values and considerable weight to values close to zero. This weighting may not be appropriate for all kinds of damages.

An emphasis on any one of these categories of effects suggests a different strategy for measuring the economic costs of air pollution. Only the last strategy, which takes into account social interactions as well as direct effects and adjustments, is adequate from a theoretical point of view. But because of data limitations, clues must be derived from wherever they can be found. Furthermore, each level of analysis can contribute to our understanding of the whole situation.

DIRECT EFFECTS: THE COST OF POLLUTION IN THE ABSENCE OF ADJUSTMENTS

If individual adjustments and social interactions are ignored, three types of information will suffice to yield the desired cost estimate. First, we must have a description of the damage per unit of each object affected as a function of the intensity of air pollution, all other factors that could cause such damage being held constant. If there are determinate relationships between such damages and the particular pollutant concerned, they can be represented as:

$$D_i = F_i(S), \quad i = (1,..,n)$$

where D_i is a measure of the i-th type of damage per unit of object affected by the pollution and S is a measure of pollution (in our example, annual geometric mean sulfation rate). In this notation each different damage to each different object must be identified separately. Second, a monetary weight (a price or a cost per unit of damage) appropriate to measure the importance of the particular effect must be obtained. And third, an indication of the number of units of the objects affected is necessary.

Assuming the monetary weights and the number of units affected stay constant as the level of pollution varies, the total cost for this pollutant can be obtained by multiplying by the appropriate cost-per-unit damage, C_i, and the number of units affected, Q_i, and then summing over all types of damage. The total cost function would then be represented by the expression:

$$\sum_{i=1}^{n} C_i Q_i F_i(S),$$

and its derivative with respect to S is the marginal cost.[2]
The following paragraphs discuss the general data requirements needed to implement this approach.

The specification of the damage function is the job of the
technical expert in the appropriate field -- the metallurgist if
we are talking about metal corrosion, the epidemiologist or
physiologist if we are concerned with damage to human beings.
But if their studies are to be useful for economic analyses,
the damage function must be specified in terms relevant to the
issue of economic loss.. Changes in human respiration rates
or in a measure of plasmolysis in plants are not useful for
this purpose, whereas changes in absenteeism rates or in
fruit yields are. To date, very little is available in a form
that is useful for economic analysis (an example of the best
available is given on p. 85). Under these circumstances,
the most that an economist can do is to indicate what is required for an economic analysis of a specific pollution problem
and then to concentrate on measuring the unit costs and the
quantities at risk.

The problems in measuring the cost of a unit of damage
vary from the trivial to the highly complex, depending on the
type of damage considered. If there is a market for the objects
of interest, the market price can serve as a useful first approximation. If there is a simple, direct way to eliminate the
damage -- for example, by repainting objects exposed to a

---

[2]Care must be taken in aggregating to avoid including costs
of adjustments or market effects (unless these are used as
proxies for the direct effects). For example, crop damage
should be included, but not changes in land values that result.
Otherwise there is a danger of double counting.

corrosive atmosphere -- the minimum cost of such maintenance or repair can be used as a conservative estimate of the
loss due to the damage. [3] If there is no market for the affected
objects, it may still be possible to construct a useful cost
figure for market data. This is the case, for example, with
some categories of effects on human beings. A minimal, but
still useful, estimate of the mortality cost of a particular disease can be obtained from market costs of treatment, burial,
and loss of earnings, if they are judiciously combined with a
wide variety of assumptions about life expectancy, employment
rates, discount rates, and the like. Chapter 3 explains how
this can be done to obtain a unit price for diseases associated
with air pollution.

But finally, there are some losses for which there are no market reflections whatsoever. The most important and difficult
example of this type of loss is what might be called "psychic
costs." This category includes everything from the anguish
of death to the disappointment felt when one's view of the
mountains is obscured by smog.

Economists have generally ignored this category on three
grounds: First, in many cases its inclusion would not alter
a decision suggested by an otherwise adequate benefit-cost
analysis; second, it cannot be accurately measured; and third,
it is, in any case, the responsibility of the electorate to place
a value on such intangibles. As for the first argument, it is
certainly true that definite policy conclusions can be reached

---

[3]Reliance on this approach implies the assumption that
people will not spend more to eliminate damage than they estimate the loss to be. This approach requires great care in
specifying the damage function. This function must, for
example, reflect the need for repainting of a house solely because of air pollution, that is, independent of the desire to
change its color and of all other motives that may be involved.
If it is purified of other causal factors in this respect, then
the above assumption is likely to be justifiable.

in some cases without considering psychic costs. Thus, if an evaluation of a health program indicates that the marginal benefits are far enough in excess of the marginal costs to compare favorably with other contemplated investment programs, the unmeasured aspects can be ignored, since their net effect will in all probability only make the program look even more attractive. But where air pollution is concerned, in some important cases the inclusion of psychic considerations would make a difference in the policy decision. The extreme case would be a pollutant that has no consequences other than bad odors or the blurring of scenic views. The second argument (that it cannot be accurately measured) has so far been made a priori; but empirical evidence on this point, such as this study seeks, is essential for a more satisfactory case. The last point implies that such estimates are not needed. The argument would have some validity if in fact the electorate did vote on such matters; but such votes are rare and when they are taken provide opportunities only for all-or-none declarations.

Within the framework of this first measurement strategy, the only way to measure psychic costs is to ask people how much they would be willing to pay to obtain a more pleasant environment. In cases where a psychic loss is the only loss involved, willingness-to-pay is a direct measure of the unit cost of this loss. In other cases, psychic costs will be the difference between the amount the subject is willing to pay and the direct resource costs incurred, assuming that the former is equal to or greater than the latter. [4]

---

[4]If a person indicates he is willing to pay less than the amount that the pollution cost him in resource terms, he must be (a) unaware of some of these nonpsychic costs (and would presumably change his answer if made aware of them), (b) misinterpreting the question, or (c) acting irrationally. The extent of such answers in a questionnaire can serve as a partial check on the usefulness of this approach.

Many questions can be raised about the validity of this approach. Can the questions be so worded that the interviewee understands and interprets them properly? Does he know what hypothetical package he really is buying with his answer? Can his suspicions that his answer may affect his taxes without affecting what he receives for them be allayed? Does he reject the idea of payment with the statement that he should receive the benefit as a right without special payment? If actually faced with the hypothetical situation posed to him -- for example in a referendum -- would he respond in the same way? Would his response a month later bear much resemblance to his response today? The doubts implied in such questions probably account for the fact that very few reasonably careful interview studies of willingness to pay for nonmarketed goods and services have been undertaken.[5] Yet these doubts can only be resolved by empirical investigation. The interview approach used in this study and reported on in Chapters 4 and 5 provides at least some evidence to suggest that this approach is useful.

The final category of information necessary to implement this first strategy involves the number of objects vulnerable to pollution damage. The problems involved in this task are few.

---

[5]Two studies by Robert K. Davis (The Value of Outdoor Recreation: An Economic Study of the Maine Woods, unpublished Ph.D. thesis, Harvard University, 1961, and "The Value of Big Game Hunting in a Private Forest," Resources for the Future, 1964, mimeo) use willingness-to-pay questions to derive demand curves for certain recreational facilities. A detailed exposition of the method and its rationale is provided in the first of these studies. Eva Mueller, in an article entitled "Public Attitudes Toward Fiscal Programs," Quarterly Journal of Economics, LXXVII, 1963, pp. 210-35, presents useful information on attitudes, discusses the advantages and disadvantages of the sample survey approach, and presents some material suggesting that attitudes toward certain fiscal programs might not be stable over time.

In some cases the data are already gathered, as for example information on the number of persons, automobiles, and houses exposed to urban environments. In other cases, sample survey methods can be used to make the necessary estimates. This is not to say that such a survey would always be easy. It would be quite costly, for example, to obtain a reasonable estimate of the extent of exposed surfaces, such as unprotected metals, that could be damaged by air pollution. But in principle, the procedure to accomplish the task is straightforward.

Since this first approach to measuring the costs of air-pollution damage leaves out adjustments and social-interaction effects, its conclusions will be biased. If all the direct costs have been measured, these biases will overstate the costs of air-pollution damage, for unless the net effect of the adjustments is to reduce the associated costs, the adjustments would not have been undertaken. Thus, in contrast to many economic analyses in the public health and human resources fields, we cannot stop at this level of analysis and be sure that we have conservatively assessed the damages. It is necessary to go to the next level and consider individual adjustments.

INDIVIDUAL ADJUSTMENTS

It is difficult to think of cases in which there are no possibilities available to adjust to a detrimental change in the environment. In the worst cases, the possibilities may not be economically very significant; but something, if only psychological adjustment, can always be done to reduce the impact of a change.

Consider a person who suddenly finds his asthma getting worse because the level of air pollution is increasing. On the most general level, he may do nothing, simply suffering the additional discomfort involved; or he may change his behavior in response to the deteriorating environment. The change in his behavior may be of three different types: First, the individual may change the amount of time he spends in the affected area, for example by taking longer vacations outside the area of his residence, by moving his place of residence, or by changing jobs. Second, without changing the amount of time spent in the affected area, he may try to offset the detrimental effects by taking some remedial action, for example by staying indoors and filtering air coming from outside or by taking additional medications. Third, without changing his location, the individual may try to achieve the removal of the added pollution from his environment. Perhaps the most obvious example here is political action to force controls on emissions. Such actions seek to eliminate the pollution, whereas the other actions try in different ways to eliminate the consequences of the pollution.

If we accept the normal assumptions about human behavior made in microeconomic theory, several implications for measurement follow. First, no matter what the individual does, he suffers a loss in utility. If he does nothing, he suffers a direct loss; if he adjusts in any way, he transfers at least some of the loss to other categories where it appears in a different form. In so doing, he may reduce the total loss, but he cannot completely eliminate it. Second, the individual will generally find that he can cut his losses by spreading them among a number of categories -- by letting his car remain a little dirtier and by washing it a little more often. Third, there is no a priori reason to assume that some categories of behavior will be so small, relative to others, that the losses resulting from them can be ignored.

These points raise serious problems for measurement. They mean that we must seek to discover all the effects of pollution damage, that we cannot, at the outset, concentrate on any one category of loss and hope thereby to obtain a reasonable approximation for the others. After the fact we may discover that certain categories of adjustments are unimportant and can be ignored, but not until the measurements have been made.

In contrast to studies based on the first approach, attempts to measure the costs of adjustment cannot rely upon a damage function provided by the pollution expert. Any relation between air pollution and the cost of adjustments to it must be based upon data specifically gathered for this purpose. In principle, the procedure is straightforward. First, each logically possible and mutually exclusive category of adjustment that will minimize the effects of a particular pollutant on a particular object must be identified, and behavior falling into these categories must be measured. Second, all important variables that could also explain this behavior must be identified and measured. These measurements must be made in such a way that changes in variables over time and space can be associated with similar variations in the pollutant. Finally, for each category of behavior statistical analysis must be applied to filter out the effects of the pollutant from the other factors that could also explain the behavior involved. The result will be the equivalent of a damage function, which must then be combined with estimates of unit costs and quantities at risk and aggregated over different categories of behavior to obtain a cost of pollution function.

This approach is illustrated in Chapter 4, which reports on a survey that, among other things, attempted to determine the extent to which maintenance and cleaning costs in the home are related to air pollution. Since this study is essentially exploratory, intended to identify differences in cleaning activities and the major factors that cause them, the questionnaire is quite long and covers a wider range of material than is normal in such studies. For example, the observed differences in the cost of keeping interior walls clean may appear as dollar costs, as a difference in frequency with which the task is performed, as time spent performing the task, as energy expended on the task, or as "psychic loss" (i.e., letting the walls get dirtier). Until some of these forms of behavior are determined to be trivial, we must continue asking about each. Furthermore, since at best air pollution is likely to explain very few of the observed variations in this set of variables,

we must go much further than the normal consumer expenditure study; we must seek information that can help separate
out other -- and probably more important -- causes of the
variation. Thus, in addition to income, education, ethnic
background, and the like the interviewee was asked whether
pets live in the house, what kind of heating system is used,
how many members of the family smoke, and so on.

As explained below, in contrast to the first strategy of
measurement, this approach involves an understatement of
the costs of pollution.

MARKET EFFECTS

Although for practical reasons it may not be possible to go
beyond the level of individual adjustments in seeking measurements, the only completely adequate way to measure the social
losses involved in levels of pollution is to take into account
social interactions -- the effect of one person's actions upon
another. Perhaps the most important interactions for our
purpose are the effects that occur because people are linked
together by their purchases and sales in different markets.
Even though you are not affected by the pollution, you may be
greatly affected by the fact that I, who am affected, alter my
market behavior.

To a large extent such market effects represent transfers
of benefits or costs between economic units rather than an additional set of consequences not taken into account (in principle at least) by the second measurement strategy. [6] For

---

[6]There are a few exceptions to this statement. If the long-
run supply function for products whose demand increases because of the increase in pollution slopes upward, additional
costs will be involved for all users; if it slopes downward,
additional benefits will result. Similarly, while the increased
pollution levels will make people who are most sensitive to
its effects move out, the market effects of their moving will
induce others who are less sensitive to move in, with a conse-

example, spinach and orchid growers at first bore the brunt of
the costs involved in not being able to produce in the Los
Angeles area; but to the extent that their prices rose as a consequence, some of these losses were transferred from the
producers to the consumers. Similarly, in the housing market, a rise in pollution in one sector of the market will result
in some offsetting fall in property values and rents in that sector and some rise in the unaffected area. In this fashion, the
market tends to spread the consequences of pollution among
individuals.

From a measurement point of view, this spreading of effects is unfortunate. First, it means that estimates of the
costs of pollution based on the second strategy of measurement in all probability understate the true costs. This method
includes only the costs of the affected individual's adjustments
and of necessity must employ market data that already incor-
porate such spreading effects; it does not include the costs
that have been transferred to those who were not initially affected by the pollution. Only if the pollution effects cannot be
transferred would the second strategy yield correct results.
Second, as explained below, such spreading effects seriously
complicate both the measurement problem and the problem of
interpreting the meaning of any estimates based upon market
data.

The proper way to measure such effects is to estimate the
change in the consumer plus producer surpluses in each market affected by the change in pollution, and to sum these surpluses over the affected markets. Since air pollution is a
sufficiently small effect that spending on it is hardly likely to
alter the marginal utility of income, these surpluses can be
adequately estimated by changes in the areas between the ag-

---

quent reduction in the costs of pollution. Such additional consequences are likely to be small and, in the face of all the
other problems, can be ignored.

gregate demand and supply curves to the left of the equilibrium point in each market.

Now, if this prescription were to be followed exactly, estimates of the demand and supply curves for every important market would have to be estimated; and for each, all other factors that could explain shifts in the curves would have to be accounted for so that any remaining variations could be explained by air pollution. This is virtually an impossible task. However, as far as air pollution is concerned, there is one market that is more likely than any other to reflect the majority of effects. This is the land, or real estate, market.

If the land market were to work perfectly, the price of a plot of land would equal the sum of the present discounted streams of benefits and costs derivable from it. If some of its costs rise (e. g. , if additional maintenance and cleaning costs are required) or if some of its benefits fall (e. g. , if one cannot see the mountains from the terrace) the property will be discounted in the market to reflect people's evaluation of these changes. Since air pollution is specific to locations and the supply of locations is fixed, there is less likelihood that the negative effects of pollution can be significantly shifted onto other markets. We should therefore expect to find the majority of effects reflected in this market, and can measure them by observing associated changes in property values.

There are a number of arguments that can be made against this strategy of measurement. First, it shares difficulties that most statistical studies of economic phenomena have in common: Markets do not work perfectly; at any one point in time we cannot be sure we are measuring equilibrium values; and it is difficult to set up an adequate statistical model that can separate out and hold constant all factors other than air pollution which can also explain the observed variations in the dependent variable. There is nothing unique about these problems; the only issue is whether they are so severe in our case that the attempt to use this method should not be made.

Unfortunately, there is no way to answer this question except by trying.

Second, it is not always clear just what is being discounted in the property values. In order for a particular consequence of air pollution to have an observable effect on property values, buyers and sellers must know that these consequences differ in different parts of the city. They need not know that air pollution causes these effects, but only that, for example, repainting is required less frequently in some areas than in others. This issue is of some importance in aggregating estimates of costs of air pollution based upon different measurement methods, for behind it is the problem of double counting. While a detailed, separate study is needed to find out just what negative consequences of pollution are being discounted,[7] the answer is likely to depend strongly upon the particular class of buyers and sellers involved. To minimize this problem, as well as to reduce the complexity of developing a

_____

[7]The type of answers normally obtained in sample surveys of householders and business firms are generally not of much help in this regard, since they typically measure awareness of and attitudes toward air pollution. Sufficient evidence is now available to indicate that families and business firms consider air pollution in their decisions as to whether and where to move (for families, see references cited in Chapter 7; for business firms, see the survey conducted by the St. Louis County Business and Industrial Development Commission in 1964 in which 30 out of 384 firms interviewed mentioned air pollution -- presumably its absence -- as one of their reasons for moving to Clayton, Missouri. None gave pollution as their most important reason, but one ranked it as his second, six as their third and three as their fourth reason in order of importance). But very little is available to indicate which of the effects of pollution are believed to be avoided by moving. Some information on this point was obtained in the household questionnaire from questions about the desirable and undesirable features of the interviewee's neighborhood, as compared to others, and is reported on in Chapter 4.

statistical model that can explain other reasons for variations
in property values, separate property value studies should be
undertaken for residential, commercial, and industrial land.
For these reasons, the property value studies included in
this volume are restricted to only the residential segment of
the whole market.

Third, and quite apart from the issue of aggregation, there
is a problem of interpreting the numerical results. Two cases
pose most of the problems. First, suppose that a city initially
consists of two identical residential areas, A and B, that an
improvement occurs in the air quality of A but not of B, and
that as a consequence property values rise in A and fall in B.
What is the appropriate monetary measure of the improvement in welfare? Is it the rise in values in A, the resulting
difference between the values in A and B times the number of
units of property in A, the rise in A minus the fall in B, or
something else altogether? Second, instead of a differential
improvement in air quality, suppose the improvement is uniform throughout the city. How can the welfare improvement be
judged in this case, when no differential in property values
will arise? [8]

These questions raise problems that are not easily resolved.
For this study it is sufficient to note that if redistribution effects are ignored and no change in land use or lot size is
assumed, the appropriate measure in the first case is the
difference between property values in A and B times the number of units of property in A:[9] Owners in A should be willing

---

[8]If no one is induced to move into or out of the city by the
change, and if property cannot be substituted for other items
in consumer budgets, there will not even be a change in the
over-all level of property values.

[9]For rigorous proofs see R. C. Lind, The Nature of Flood
Control Benefits and the Economics of Flood Protection, Stan-
ford University, 1966, and R. H. Strotz, Economics of Urban
Air Pollution, Resources for the Future, 1966.

to pay at least this much for the improvement (i.e., to keep
their houses from becoming like those in B). In the second
case we can only apply information obtained from areas
where a differential has been observed, assuming that the
unit difference can be applied to all units experiencing the improvements. Since it must be justified by special assumptions
that are not always met, this resolution of the problems of
interpreting the numerical results from property value studies
is not completely satisfactory. More work remains to be done
on these issues. Despite these problems, the potential advantage of using property values is great, for it represents a way
to capture in one figure a diverse group of psychic and resource
costs associated with real estate that otherwise must be estimated separately. For this reason two property value studies
are included in this volume, and the household survey discussed
in Chapter 4 attempts to shed some light on just what is being
discounted in these property values. (See p. 139 on this point.)

A PREVIEW OF THE MEASUREMENT STUDIES

The various approaches outlined in this chapter represent
strategies for measuring the costs of pollution on a fairly
general level. Once we enter the field, special tactics must be
devised to cope with more detailed problems, and it is easy to
lose sight of the general approaches and their significance.
The following sketch is intended to prevent this by indicating
which studies represent applications of which strategies.

Chapter 3 clearly fits under the first strategy of measurement; its main purpose is to develop price or cost weights for
different diseases. The second strategy is represented by the
next two chapters. The series of studies presented in Chapter
4 have several things in common. They are all concerned with
adjustments to soiling and materials damage effects of air pollution in normal urban settings, and unfortunately, they all
reach negative or inconclusive results. The first section of
this chapter presents studies of business and commercial
establishments and the second summarizes the results of an

attempt to develop and implement a household questionnaire to measure pollution-related cleaning and maintenance costs. In the third section the reasons for these negative findings are discussed and a proposal is made that should help provide the desired evidence in the future. Chapter 5 presents the results of a more successful household survey; in this case, however, pollution levels rose to abnormally high levels for a short period. The third strategy of measurement, based on observed market adjustments to pollution, is applied in Chapters 6 and 7. Both attempt to find an association between property values and air pollution, but the first relies on currently available cross-section data and the second on time-series data gathered in conjunction with a special pollution incident.

It is unfortunate that all three strategies could not be applied to at least one category of effects of a specific pollutant so that their results could be compared. Data limitations, which compel a certain opportunism in selecting measurement studies, preclude this. The proposal made at the end of Chapter 4 is partially aimed at solving this problem.

3

ECONOMIC COSTS OF DISEASES ASSOCIATED WITH AIR POLLUTION*

This chapter attempts to identify and measure the economic costs of a number of diseases that are judged by medical and public health experts to be related to air pollution. Since there is no accepted body of evidence that permits us to establish a quantitative relationship between disease rates and specific pollutant levels, it is not possible to derive a complete cost-of-pollution curve for this category of effects. The best that can be done is to estimate the average and total costs of these diseases and to suggest roughly the magnitude of the costs that might be the result of air pollution. Once the relationship between health and air pollution becomes better understood, unit cost figures derived in the manner of this chapter can be used to assign dollar magnitudes to this category of air-pollution effects, and thus to derive a cost function for them. The cost estimates in this chapter are incomplete because of data limitations, but the method used to derive them can be applied when new categories of information become available in the future.

AIR POLLUTION AND POOR HEALTH

A brief review of what is known and suspected about the health effects of air pollution will place the cost estimates to be derived here in context. Evidence about the association of air pollution and health comes from three sources: (1) studies

---

*Dr. Alphonse Haltmann is the principal author of the unit cost estimates presented in this chapter.

30

made of a number of severe episodes that have occurred at various times throughout the world; (2) epidemiological studies of persons and communities subject to low levels of pollution for extended periods of time; and (3) laboratory studies of humans and animals in experimental environments. [1]

Studies of severe episodes such as occurred in the Meuse Valley in 1930, in Yokohama in 1946, Donora, Pennsylvania, in 1948, and London in 1952 and 1962 leave little doubt that abnormally high levels of air pollution (in particular sulfur dioxide and smoke or dust) can increase mortality and morbidity rates for diseases associated with the respiratory system. For example, an additional 3,500 to 4,000 deaths from chronic bronchitis, broncho-pneumonia, and heart disease have been attributed to the London episode of 1952. Many of these deaths occurred among those who already had the diseases or were more sensitive due to the presence of other illnesses, age, or other factors. However, some American servicemen and their dependents appear to have actually contracted chronic obstructive respiratory diseases during their stay in Yokohama at the end of World War II. This evidence is particularly striking because in many cases the symptoms disappeared once the men were moved to another environment. [2]

---

[1] A good summary of what is known about air-pollution effects on humans is contained in John R. Goldsmith, "Effects of Air Pollution on Humans," Vol. I, Chap. 10, of Arthur C. Stern (Ed.), Air Pollution (New York: Academic Press, 1962), pp. 335-83. Also see John R. Goldsmith, "Effects of Air Pollution on Man," Connecticut Medicine, 27, 8 (August, 1963), pp. 455 ff. Unless otherwise noted, information for this section of Chapter 3 comes from these sources.

[2] Eric J. Cassell, "The Unsolved Problem: The Effect of Air Pollution on Human Health," mimeo (Cornell University Medical College, New York, 1963), p. 16, and personal discussion with Dr. Charles R. Sharp.

Although the effects of chronic, but lower levels of exposure are less certain, evidence is slowly accumulating that suggests an association between such levels of pollution in urban communities and mortality and morbidity rates due to lung and bronchial cancer, chronic bronchitis, emphysema, asthma, and pneumonia.[3] Most of this evidence comes from epidemiological studies that are beset with problems of detection, inadequate air-pollution data, the mobility of the populations being studied, and the fact that these same diseases appear to be associated with other factors which may be more important determinants than air pollution (weather conditions, smoking habits, socio-economic class, and occupational exposure to such materials as cooking fats, gasoline and oils, coal dust, road dust, and welding fumes). As a consequence independent epidemiological studies sometimes produce conflicting results that are so at variance with other evidence that no quantitative statements about the extent of the associations are justified. Nevertheless, most experts seem to agree that respiratory disease rates are higher for persons whose occupation, place of residence, or level of activity brings them into more than average contact with pollutants normally found in urban areas.

---

[3]In addition to the articles by Goldsmith, see Clarence A. Mills, Air Pollution and Community Health (Boston: The Christopher Publishing House, 1954); Cassell and Reinhard Poche, Otfrid Mittmann and Oswald Kneller, "Statistische Untersuchungen uber das Bronchialcarcinom in Nordhein-Westfalen," Zeitschrift fur Krebsforschung, 66 (1964), pp. 87-108. Also see Louis D. Zeidberg, Robert J. M. Horton and Emanuel Landau, "The Nashville Air Pollution Study: V. Mortality from Diseases of the Respiratory System in Relation to Air Pollution," (mimeo, presented before the Epidemiology Section of the American Public Health Association, Kansas City, Missouri, November 12, 1963) and references cited there.

In addition to such serious diseases, problems such as excessive rates of eye irritation, throat irritation, and colds also have been mentioned as being associated with increased levels of air pollution. [4]

Laboratory studies support the same contentions. [5] Many tars that have been extracted from sooty air are capable of causing cancer in animals. Physiological tests have shown that sulfur dioxide, dilute motor exhaust, and similar irritants increase the resistance to air flow into and out of the lungs of humans and animals, thereby increasing the work of breathing. The inhalation of even low concentrations of carbon monoxide can raise the level of carboxyhemoglobin to a point where it is seen to interfere with the transportation of oxygen in the blood stream. While these studies do not directly link air pollution with respiratory diseases, they do suggest that pollutants can aggravate existing lung and heart diseases, handicap particularly sensitive persons (such as premature infants, the aged, and those recovering from surgery or weakened by other illnesses) and, by generally increasing the body burden of potentially harmful substances, shorten the normal person's lifespan.

Given these facts and hypotheses, and considering the data limitations, cost estimates for the following diseases are developed: (1) cancer of the respiratory system, (2) chronic and

[4]Goldsmith, op. cit., p. 368; Harry Heimann, et. al., "Health and Air Pollution -- A Study on a Limited Budget," Transactions of the American Conference of Government Industrial Hygiene, 13th Annual Meeting, 1951, pp. 19-24; and Tuberculosis and Health Association of Los Angeles County, Los Angeles County Medical Association, "Physicians' Environmental Health Survey, A Pool of Medical Opinion," mimeo, May 1961.

[5]Richard A. Prindle and Emanuel Landau, "Health Effects from Repeated Exposures to Low Concentrations of Air Pollutants," mimeo, presented before the Verein Deutscher Ingenieure Commission, June 20, 1962, Dusseldorf, Germany.

acute bronchitis, (3) pneumonia, (4) emphysema, and (5) asthma. The common cold has also been included because despite its more tenuous link with air pollution, its economic costs are, in the aggregate, larger than for some other diseases.

THE ECONOMIC COST OF A DISEASE

The costs of a disease may be classified according to four categories: those due to premature death, those associated with morbidity, those incurred for treatment, and those incurred for prevention or avoidance. If this classification system is to be adequate, it must include all types of costs whether they are direct or indirect, material or psychic; it must include the losses incurred by the affected individual, by others associated with him, and by society as a whole; and it must include these losses no matter in what form they occur, provided, of course, no double counting is involved.

Without going into detail, the nature of these requirements can be illustrated by considering the case of a man who becomes ill with a respiratory infection. If he continues to work, he is uncomfortable, may make others uncomfortable, probably works less efficiently, and may infect others. If he stays at home and rests, he affects others to a lesser degree and possibly recovers more quickly, but his economic productivity is zero. If he purchases drugstore remedies or professional help, he raises his dollar outlays, but he may recover more rapidly and will probably suffer less discomfort in the process. If the illness is believed to be caused by avoidable environmental factors and if it recurs often enough or is sufficiently severe, he and others who fear being affected may change their place of residence, in which case moving costs and possibly a lower level of earnings are involved. [6] In many cases

---

[6]According to a 1960 survey of physicians in Los Angeles, over 10,000 patients were advised to leave the Los Angeles

some combination of these methods of attempting to spread and minimize the losses will be found. A comprehensive estimate of the costs of a disease would require data for each of these different methods.

Data limitations and the conceptual difficulty of valuing human life make it impossible to measure more than a few of the types of losses that occur. In particular this study emphasizes the resource losses involved in the first three categories of costs. Avoidance costs and whatever psychic costs are involved in different categories are left out. These omissions, plus less important ones indicated below, make the figures presented here underestimate the total costs of these diseases related to air pollution.[7]

The Costs of Premature Death

Loss of Output

When a person dies, society loses the output that he would have produced had he not died prematurely. But society also loses a consumer, and it could be argued that what is lost is the amount of output the deceased could have produced minus his consumption. The choice between these measures of loss depends on our definition of society.[8] If we include the person

---

area and at least 2,500 acted upon this advice during 1960. See Tuberculosis and Health Association of Los Angeles County, op. cit., pp. 6-7.

[7]A reasonable argument can be made that psychic costs are sufficiently correlated with monetary costs so that the latter can be used as an index for the total costs associated with the first three categories. See Burton A. Weisbrod, Economics of Public Health (Philadelphia: University of Pennsylvania Press, 1961), pp. 96-98. A similar argument could also be made for avoidance costs.

[8]For two differing views on this matter see: Weisbrod, op. cit., pp. 35-36, who uses the net output approach, and Rashi Fein, Economics of Mental Illness (New York: Basic Books, 1958), pp. 18-19.

who has died as part of society, then we should use total output as the measure of the loss to society; but if we consider all
others except the individual who dies as the society, output
net of consumption is the appropriate measure of loss.

This study uses the total output approach. First, it is
more appealing in that it permits the assumption that society
is composed of all its members and that none of them has negative value, as would be the case for some if the net output
approach were used. Second, roughly as much is spent to
keep alive persons whose value in net output terms is expected
to be zero or negative as is spent for persons whose value in
these terms is positive. Ignoring psychic losses, this behavior is more consistent with the total than the net output
approach, for the latter suggests that society should not interfere with the death of a person whose net value is negative.

To estimate the loss of output that accompanies the premature death of an individual we must attempt to estimate the present value of all future output that could be attributed to that individual. The best measure of an individual's contribution to
output at any given time is his wage. Although this is not a perfectly accurate measure unless the economy conforms to the
assumptions of the perfectly competitive model, it represents
the best single estimate available.[9]

Since these earnings are uncertain to be forthcoming in the
future, we must also know the probability that an individual
will live to any future age and, if he lives, will be productive.
Average earnings at each future age must be multiplied by
this joint probability to obtain the expected value of future earnings for an individual of any given age.

---

[9]Among the various assumptions of the perfectly competitive model is that of full employment. Actually, we do not
assume full employment, but rather, that the 1960 unemployment rates will continue to prevail in the future. See below.

It is clear, however, that the sum of the expected future earnings of an individual is not the present value of the lost earnings due to premature death. As long as a positive rate of interest prevails in the economy, any future earnings must be discounted by the prevailing rate of interest. This is due to the fact that a dollar in earnings in the future is worth less than a dollar at present because of the productivity of capital and the apparent cost of postponing consumption. Therefore, all future earnings must be discounted by an appropriate rate of interest to determine the present value of future earnings lost due to premature death.

These concepts are reflected in the following formula:[10]

$$V_a = \sum_{n=a}^{\infty} \frac{P_{a_1}^n \cdot P_{a_2}^n \cdot P_{a_3}^n \cdot Y_n}{(1 + r)^{n-a}}$$

where

V_a is the present value of the future earnings of an individual age a;

$P_{a_1}^n$ is the probability that an individual age a will live to age n;

$P_{a_2}^n$ is the probability that an individual age a living to age n will be in the labor force at age n;

$P_{a_3}^n$ is the probability that an individual age a living and in the labor force at age n will be employed at age n;

Y_n is the earnings at age n; and

r is the rate of interest.

_____

[10]This formula is essentially the same as that used by Weisbrod (op. cit., p. 40).

The three probability figures in this formula were calculated from age-specific data on life expectancy, labor force participation rates, and the unemployment rates for the 1960 population. The estimation procedure for obtaining Y_n and r involves a number of conceptual issues requiring special discussion.

Turning first to the earnings estimates, several special problems must be dealt with. First, the average earnings figures by age were obtained by weighting together the different occupation-specific earnings figures available for the experienced labor force for each age. This degree of aggregation, unfortunately, was made necessary by the fact that only age-specific disease rates were available.

Second, statistics on wage rates measure only what an individual produces in the market. But when we mow our lawn, paint our house, service our car, etc., we are producing items or services of value just as if we had been paid to perform these tasks for someone else. The procedure followed in this study is to leave out such nonmarket production. The resulting understatement is not serious so far as males are concerned, but may be substantial in the case of women. The problem posed by the fact that a large part of the services of women do not go through the market is discussed in Appendix A, p. 163.

Interest rates of 5 and 10 per cent have been chosen for this study. The data in most tables is for both rates, though 5 per cent is used as the basis for the discussion in the text. [11]

---

[11]Two rates are used to determine how sensitive the final estimates are to changes in the discount rate. The lower rate has been suggested by Otto Eckstein as the appropriate rate for use with public investment expenditures. See his book, Water-Resource Development: The Economics of Project Evaluation (Cambridge: Harvard University Press, 1958), p. 99. The 10 per cent figure is the midpoint of the range

The results of applying the foregoing formula are summarized in Table 1 and presented in detail in Tables 1 through 7
of Appendix B, pp. 165 ff.

Table 1 and the tables in Appendix B show the present
value of male and female earnings based upon these considerations for ages 10 through 74. This age range was used because after age 74 discounted earnings are approximately zero
and before age 10 we assumed there is insufficient time for
exposure to air pollution to cause serious damage. [12]

Burial Costs

One factor in the cost of death that has been neglected in
the literature until recently are the burial costs. If a death
is postponed, society delays using resources for burial. The
gain thereby obtained is the difference between the present
cost of burial and the present value of the future expected
cost of burial. This can be calculated from the following
formula:

$$C_a = C_o \left[1 - \sum_{n=a}^{\infty} \left(\frac{P_a^n}{(1+r)^{n-a}} \right) \right]$$

---

suggested by Gary Becker as the average rate of return on
private capital in Human Capital (New York: Columbia
University Press, 1964), p. 120. Of the two, we prefer the
lower rate since, first, increasing amounts of public funds
are likely to be invested in air-pollution control and second,
our methods do not correct for labor productivity increases
over time. On the second point, the absence of past data on
age-specific rates of productivity increases led us to assume,
implicitly, that a person who is twenty today will earn the
same amount in ten years as a person who is thirty today.

[12]After the computations for this chapter were completed
this assumption was questioned by pollution experts. In future
studies it would be useful to present alternative estimates
that carry the computations back to birth.

Table 1

PRESENT VALUE OF LOST EARNINGS DUE TO DEATH FROM SELECTED DISEASES

Loss, $

Disease	5% Discount Rate				10% Discount Rate			
	Total		Average		Total		Average	
	Male	Female	Male	Female	Male	Female	Male	Female
Cancer	495,687,600	22,219,800	18,700	5,400	378,063,300	16,388,900	14,200	4,000
Chronic Bronchitis	16,126,000	1,526,400	13,700	5,600	12,285,500	1,052,600	10,400	3,900
Acute Bronchitis	4,541,200	1,163,100	19,900	7,800	3,177,600	778,200	13,600	5,200
Emphysema	60,226,800	2,164,600	12,900	4,300	47,286,200	1,591,600	10,100	3,200
Asthma	49,378,500	10,170,800	18,600	7,900	36,465,700	6,975,700	13,700	5,500
Pneumonia	287,352,800	41,825,600	20,600	5,700	204,062,900	28,477,600	14,600	3,900

Source: Appendix Tables 2 to 7.

where

C_a is the present value of the net expected gain from
delaying burial at age a;

C_0 is the cost of burial;

P_a^n is the probability an individual age a will die at
age n; and

r is the discount rate.

With the aid of this formula, the average cost of burial in 1960,
and 1960 mortality tables, we estimated the cost of premature
burial for individuals ages zero to 85. [13] These estimates are
shown in Table 8 of Appendix B for discount rates of 5 and
10 per cent. They were computed on the basis of an average
cost of burial in 1960 of $942 per burial. [14]

---

[13] The procedures used are based on those discussed in
A. G. Holtmann and R. Ridker, "Burial Costs and Premature
Death," Journal of Political Economy (June, 1965), pp. 284-86,
the only difference being that here burial costs are held constant for each age, whereas they are allowed to vary in the
referenced paper. This difference does not materially affect
the results.

Mortality data were available only up to age 85; see
U.S. Department of Health, Education and Welfare, Public
Health Service, "Life Tables," Vital Statistics of the United
States, 1960, Vol. 2, Section 2 (Washington, D.C.: U.S.
Government Printing Office, 1960), pp. 2-9. We therefore
assumed that all those living at age 85 died by the end of that
year. This causes the estimates of the cost of premature
burial to be below the true values. However, the magnitude
of the error should not be large because the probability of
dying after age 85 is high for the later years of life, and because the discounting process makes losses after age 85
rather small for the earlier years of life.

[14] Jessica Mitford, "Undertakers Racket," The Atlantic
Monthly, Vol. 211 (June, 1963), pp. 56-62.

The total cost of burial due to premature death by diseases was obtained by multiplying the age-specific burial costs by the number of deaths for that age. Only deaths after age ten were included in this calculation. It is clear from Table 2 which presents these estimates that, while losses from this cause are relatively small, they are by no means insignificant. For example, the burial cost due to premature death from cancer of the respiratory system is approximately $15 million, using a 5 per cent discount rate.

Cost of Treatment

The cost of treatment of the diseases considered here is much more difficult to estimate than the cost of death from these diseases. In many cases, there are no data concerning the number of persons with a disease, and very little information concerning the cost of treatment is available. This is the type of data that might easily be collected by hospitals and would be a major contribution to studies concerning the cost of illness. Attempts at estimating the treatment cost of four of the diseases mentioned, plus the cost of treating the common cold are presented below. Data on the cost of treatment for emphysema and acute bronchitis are too sparse to permit comparable estimates.

Cancer of the Respiratory System

Surprising as it may seem, there are no data concerning the number of persons treated for cancer of the respiratory system, or the cost of this treatment for the year 1958. The approximate cost of treatment for 1958 is estimated here on the basis of data on the number of new cancer cases in the United States in 1953, estimated at 500,000 new cases. [15]

-----

[15]Health Inquiry, Hearing before the Committee on Interstate and Foreign Commerce, House of Representatives, Eighty-Third Congress, First Session (Washington, D.C.: U.S. Government Printing Office, 1953), Part I, p. 228.

Table 2

BURIAL COSTS OF PREMATURE DEATH
FOR SELECTED DISEASES[a]

Disease	Burial Costs, $	
	Males	Females
Cancer of the Respiratory System	12, 806, 844	2, 364, 599
Pneumonia	7, 664, 191	4, 853, 093
Chronic Bronchitis	567, 183	177, 503
Acute Bronchitis	115, 877	97, 099
Emphysema	2, 176, 934	283, 022
Asthma	1, 328, 799	803, 794

Sources: Computed from data in Appendix Table 8 and data given in Vital Statistics of the United States, 1958, Vol. 2.

[a] The estimates are slightly below the true cost for individuals over ten years of age because zero values were given to premature deaths after age 85.

Approximately 52 per cent of these cases were females and
48 per cent were males. Of course, this is an estimate of
the total number of cancer cases, and we are only interested in
those cases that were due to cancer of the respiratory system.
A study of morbidity from cancer in the U.S. during 1947 indicates that 12 per cent of all newly diagnosed cases of cancer
among men were found to be cancer of the respiratory system,
compared with 2.5 per cent of new cases among women. [16]
On this basis it can be estimated that about 28,800 males and
6,500 females had cancer of the respiratory system in 1953.
With adjustments for the increase in cancer mortality between
1953 and 1958, 39,152 males and 8,035 females over age ten
can be estimated to suffer from this disease.

Weisbrod has estimated that it cost approximately $700 per
patient for all cancer patients in 1953. [17] This estimate includes the cost of treatment and/or diagnosis. It is consistent
with an estimate of $675 as the average hospital cost of a
cancer patient in 1961, made by the National Health Education
Committee, Inc. [18] Although the cost of treatment will vary
due to the location of the cancer, $763 is used here as the best
approximation of the average cost of treating a case of cancer
of the respiratory system in 1958. This figure results from
adjusting Weisbrod's estimates for changes in the cost of medical care since 1953.

With these data, the total cost of treatment for cancer of
the respiratory system in 1958 is estimated to be approximately $35 million: for males approximately $29 million
(39,152 x $763), and for females approximately $6 million
(8,035 x $763).

---

[16]S. J. Cutler Dorn, Morbidity from Cancer in the United
States, Public Health Monograph No. 29, 1955, p. 20.

[17]Weisbrod, op. cit., p. 79

[18]Personal communication from the U.S. Department of
Health, Education and Welfare, dated May 28, 1964.

Chronic Bronchitis

In 1958, it was reported that approximately 1,264,000 persons were medically attended for chronic bronchitis between July, 1957 and June, 1958. [19] Although no information is available to indicate how many of these people were hospitalized, the number who reported bed-disability days due to their illness is known. The U.S. Public Health Service reported that 595,000 persons who had been medically attended during the 1957-58 period had experienced at least one bed-disability day during that period. It was also reported that 669,000 persons who were medically attended during that period had no bed-disability during the period. [20] To measure the cost of treating these patients it was assumed here that persons with bed-disability days were treated as outpatients. Because we are only concerned with those individuals over age ten, these data are adjusted by the percentage of individuals with this disease over age ten. This yields an estimate of 416,500 persons receiving medical care and experiencing a bed-disability day, and 468,000 receiving medical care.

The assumption concerning the distribution of treatment costs may not throw the estimates off as far as one might think. While it is unlikely that all those who had a disability day and were attented medically were hospitalized, we are concerned here with the cost of treatment whether it is given in a hospital or not. It may well be that some persons elected to go to the hospital and have treatment while others had treatment on an outpatient basis and spent time in bed at

_____

[19]Department of Health, Education and Welfare, Public Health Service, Health Statistics, Chronic Respiratory Conditions Reported in Interviews, U.S., July 1957-June 1958 (Washington, D.C.: U.S. Government Printing Office, 1959), p. 18; cited hereafter as Health Statistics.

[20]Health Statistics, p. 18.

home. The care that individuals receive at home comes at a cost, just as does care in a hospital. The cost of hospital care is used here as the best estimate of the cost of care for those requiring a bed during the year and who needed medical care.

As an estimate of the average total cost of treating a case of chronic bronchitis on an inpatient basis, we have used the average hospital and physician charges per patient reported by the Dependent's Medical Care Program of the U.S. Government.[21] According to its report for the fiscal year 1958, the average cost per person of treating bronchitis on an inpatient basis was $169. Due to lack of data concerning the cost of out-patient care, the average cost of the attending physician is used as the best available estimate of the cost of outpatient care. The average cost per patient for the attending physician's services was reported to be $41 by the Dependent's Medical Care Program. This estimate may not be too high because it does not include the cost of services provided by other physicians in the hospital who may have produced special services.

With these data, the total treatment cost for chronic bronchitis during the year 1958 may be estimated. For those who were medically attended and had at least one bed-disability day during the 1957-58 period, the total treatment cost is estimated at $70,388,500 (416,500 x $169). For those who were just medically attended during this period, the total cost of treatment is $19,188,000 (468,300 x $41). These treatment costs are rather high, and they serve as a reminder that the cost of diseases may be substantial, even though the disease kills relatively few people.

---

[21]Dependent's Medical Care Program, Second Annual Report (Denver: Office of Dependent's Medical Care, 1959), p. 80; cited hereafter as Dependent's Medical Care.

Asthma

Between July, 1957 and June, 1958, 3,946,000 persons were estimated to suffer from asthma. Of these, 2,128,000 individuals had had medical attention within the last year.[22] Although no data was available concerning the number of individuals suffering with asthma that had medical attention and were restricted to bed during at least one day of the year, this information was obtained for individuals suffering from asthma or hay fever (or both). It is assumed that the percentage of patients who had at least one bed-disability day during this year, and who had medical care, would be the same for asthma as for asthma and hay fever. With this assumption, it was estimated that approximately 544,768 asthma patients had medical care and at least one bed-disability day during the year. As in the case of chronic bronchitis, this information was used to estimate the number of patients over ten years of age incurring the cost of outpatient or inpatient care. As mentioned before, this does not mean that the persons suffering a bed-disability day and receiving medical care were actually in the hospital. It merely means that the hospital cost of treating an asthma patient is the best dollar estimate of the cost born by these persons or their families.

Again data provided by the Dependent's Medical Care Program were used to estimate the cost of treating the average case of asthma. They reported that for the fiscal year 1958, a case of asthma cost $187 to treat on an inpatient basis. It was estimated that $39 of this cost was for the attending physician.[23] The average total cost was used here to estimate the cost of inpatient care and the average cost of the attending physician to estimate the cost of outpatient care. Combining these cost estimates with those of the number of individuals

---

[22]Health Statistics, p. 3.

[23]Dependent's Medical Care, p. 80.

enduring the cost of outpatient and inpatient care, it was estimated that the total cost of outpatient care during this year
was $51,866,685 (1,329,915 x $39), and the total cost of those
who bore the cost of care and, also, at least one bed-disability day, was $85,572,135 (457,605 x $187). The treatment of
asthma is more costly than that of chronic bronchitis because
more people are affected by this disease.

Pneumonia

The total cost of treating individuals over age ten for pneumonia in 1958 is estimated from data concerning the incidence
of that disease between June, 1962 and July, 1963.[24] On the
basis of data adjusted for the number of individuals having the
disease who would be over ten years of age, and for the fact
that fewer individuals died of pneumonia in 1958 than in 1962,
it is estimated that 775,757 males and 746,655 females over
ten years of age had this disease in 1958. To gain an estimate
of the cost of treatment, those persons who died of the disease
during that year are assumed to receive the equivalent of inpatient care and the rest are assumed to receive outpatient
care. Combining this with cost estimates obtained, as before,
from the Dependent's Medical Care Program, the total cost
among males of inpatient care is $4,881,050 ($205 x 23,810) and
of outpatient care at $33,085,668 ($44 x 751,947). Among
females the costs were $3,466,550 ($205 x 16,910) and
$32,108,780 ($44 x 729,745) respectively.[25] While the estimates are by no means precise, they give one some idea of the
magnitude of the total cost of treating individuals suffering
with this disease. The difficulty in estimating the total cost

----

[24]Current Estimates from the Health Interview Survey,
United States - July 1962-June 1963, U.S. Public Health
Service Publication No. 1000, Series 10, No. 5 (January, 1964),
p. 6; cited hereafter as Current Estimates.

[25]Number of persons treated based upon data from Vital
Statistics of the United States, 1958, Vol. 2.

of treating this, as well as other diseases, reflects the poor
data available concerning the cost of treatment.

Common Cold

Although people do not usually die from the effects of the
common cold, many contract this disease each year, and,
therefore, the expenditures for treatment are substantial.
With the aid of data concerning the dollar value of drug ship-
ments by all manufacturers in 1958, one of the major drug
manufacturers in the U.S. estimates that approximately $200
million was spent on products for the treatment of coughs and
colds.[26] This estimate does not include expenditures for as-
pirin, nor any expenditures for physician's services attributable to colds. Nevertheless, the $200 million figure is used
here as a conservative estimate of the total cost of treating
colds in 1958. It should be noted that this cost of treatment
in total is higher than the cost of treatment or death from
some more lethal diseases discussed earlier.

Absenteeism

The disabling effects of the common cold and the other diseases under discussion will be partially reflected by the economic cost of absenteeism associated with this disease. Of
course, the loss of the absentee's output is only part of the
cost of absenteeism. In a society where there is so much in-
terdependence in the production of goods and services, other
individuals are likely to be less productive because of the
absence of a fellow worker. In this section, however, we are
concerned only with the direct loss of output due to absenteeism. Moreover, the estimates presented here will further
understate the economic costs of disease because they exclude
from consideration those persons not employed.

---

[26]Correspondence with Eli Lilly and Company, Economic
Studies Department, dated August 25, 1964.

Here again, as for the costs of treatment, data on emphysema and acute bronchitis are too sparce to permit comparable treatment.

Cancer of the Respiratory System

The approximate period of disability for all cancer cases is used as an estimate of the time lost from work due to cancer of the respiratory system. Weisbrod estimated that a cancer patient is disabled for about ten months. Of course, after this period some patients will die, while others are rehabilitated. At any rate, it is assumed that cancer patients lose five-sixths of their annual earnings due to disability.[27] The number of employed individuals thought to have contracted cancer of the respiratory system in 1958 was thus multiplied by five-sixths of their average annual earnings.[28] This method yields a total cost of absenteeism among males of $107,084,406 ($3,562 x 30,063), and among females of $4,270,577 ($1,937 x 2,271).[29] It is obvious that these costs are more important than the cost associated with treating the disease.

Chronic Bronchitis

During the period from July, 1957, to June, 1958, the U.S. Public Health Service estimated that approximately 16,000 persons missed work on a typical day due to chronic bronchitis.[30] Assuming, then, that approximately 16,000 man-

---

[27]Weisbrod, op. cit., p. 73.

[28]Average annual earnings were estimated by computing the weighted average annual earnings for those dying of cancer of the respiratory system in 1958.

[29]Absenteeism data from Vital Statistics of the United States, 1958, Vol 2.

[30]Health Statistics, p. 8.

years of work were lost in 1958 due to chronic bronchitis, the
cost of absenteeism can be estimated by multiplying the number
of man-years by the average annual earnings of all males and
females over fourteen years of age suffering from the disease
between July, 1957, and June, 1958. On this basis the total cost
is $52, 160, 000 ($3, 260 x 16, 000). Individuals suffering from
chronic bronchitis during 1958 will, no doubt, lose days of
work in the future due to this disease. The extent of this future loss will depend on many factors, including levels of air
pollution present in future years. Unfortunately, this loss
cannot be estimated at present.

Asthma

During the same period mentioned above, it was estimated
that 37, 000 individuals missed work on a typical day due to
asthma-hay fever. From data supplied by the Public Health
Service, it can be estimated that 49 per cent of persons with
asthma or hay fever had asthma.[31] Therefore, the average
annual earnings for individuals over fourteen years of age suffering with asthma or hay fever is multiplied by 18, 130 man
years to yield an estimated loss of $59, 919, 650 ($3, 305 x
18, 130) for absenteeism from asthma. It should be mentioned
that to add the cost from absenteeism from chronic bronchitis
and asthma would involve double counting because an individual
might have lost a day's work while suffering from both diseases. Such cases were counted twice in the interviews conducted by the Public Health Service.

Pneumonia

Although estimates of the number of work days lost in 1958
due to pneumonia were not available, some information exists
for the period between July, 1962 to June, 1963. During that
period, it was estimated that males had 8, 710, 000 and females

---

[31]Health Statistics, p. 3.

14, 995, 000 bed-disability days due to disease. [32] Based on
a 248-day work year, an estimated 91 per cent of these days
were work days. The estimated number of work days lost in
1962-63 is then adjusted by the percentage change in deaths
from pneumonia between 1958 and 1962, and for the fact that
some of the bed-days lost would be by individuals that were
either not in the labor force or unemployed. If these data are
converted to man-years of work lost, and multiplied by the
average annual earnings of those individuals of working age
who died with pneumonia in 1958, the resulting total loss estimate is $54, 395, 670 ($3, 990 x 13, 633) for males and
$20, 642, 024 ($2, 132 x 9, 682) for females.

Common Cold

Essentially the same procedure used to estimate the absenteeism loss due to pneumonia was used to estimate absenteeism losses from the common cold. It was reported that males
suffered 38, 474, 000 bed-disability days during the period July,
1962-June, 1963, and that females suffered 58, 793, 000 bed-
disability days during the same period. [33] If these estimates
are converted to man-years of work lost in 1958, and multiplied by the average annual earnings of persons dying with
acute upper respiratory ailments in 1958, the resulting estimate of total loss by absenteeism due to the common cold is
$86, 328, 900 ($4, 053 x 21, 300) for men and $44, 619, 687
($2, 149 x 20, 763) for females. Although these estimates are
quite large, they are smaller than other estimates of this loss
which have been made.

Total Costs

Table 3 presents a summary of these economic costs. As
expected, cancer of the respiratory system is the most costly

---

[32]Current Estimates, p. 6.

[33]Current Estimates, p. 6.

of these diseases. But it is interesting to note how expensive are pneumonia and the common cold relative to chronic and acute bronchitis and emphysema. In large measure these cost differentials can be explained by differences in incidence rates at different ages between these diseases.

Summing across the last row of Table 3 yields a total economic cost figure for these diseases of over $1,989 million in 1958. Almost half of this amount ($964 million, obtained by summing the items in the second two rows of Table 3) represents a direct loss in output in that year. The remainder ($1,025 million) represents the destruction of productive assets -- mostly human capital -- that was caused by these diseases in 1958. Had these assets not been destroyed they could have produced an additional $51 million ($1,025 million x the .05 discount rate) in output each year.

Two bases of comparison can be used to indicate the magnitude of these figures. The loss in productive assets can be compared to the $25 billion addition to the economy's physical capital stock, recorded in the U.S. national accounts for 1958. This comparison, however, is not completely adequate because investment in human capital is not included in the national accounts figure. Alternatively, if the cost figures are expressed in terms of the loss in total output they represent, they can be compared to net national product. If there had been no cases of these diseases in 1958, net national product could have been $1,015 million larger in that year and $51 million larger in every subsequent year.[34] Since net national product was $405.9 billion in 1958, this does not represent a very substantial percentage loss in that year alone. However, to these figures must be added the losses due to cases of

_____

[34]The figure of $1,015 million is obtained by adding $51 million to the direct loss in output of $964 million, and by ignoring the time lag due to the fact that all cases of the diseases did not occur at the beginning of the year.

Table 3

RESOURCE COSTS OF DISEASES ASSOCIATED WITH AIR POLLUTION

Type of Cost	Cancer of the Respiratory System	Chronic Bronchitis	Acute Bronchitis	Common Cold	Pneumonia	Emphysema	Asthma
	Costs Associated with Selected Diseases, [a]Millions of $						
Premature Death	518	18	6	na	329	62	59
Premature Burial	15	0.7	0.2	na	13	2	2
Treatment	35	89	na	200	73	na	138
Absenteeism	112	52	na	131	75	na	60
Total	680	159.7	6.2	331	490	64	259

Source: Appendix Tables 2 through 8 and Table 2.

[a]Using a discount rate of 5 per cent.

these diseases occurring during 1959, and so on into the future. The cumulative loss in potential output over a few years' time could be substantial.

Furthermore, it must be remembered that these estimates are very conservative. We have estimated only the monetary value of the resources lost due to diseases related to air pollution, excluding avoidance costs; and nothing has been included to represent the value of the human lives lost. In addition, the value of lost housewife services has been left out; no data were available for treatment and absenteeism costs of acute bronchitis and emphysema; and a number of assumptions had to be made which further reduced the magnitude of the final figures. This underestimation is unfortunate, but since some bias is inevitable, it is better to know definitely what its direction is than to introduce assumptions, whose direction of influence is unknown.

AIR POLLUTION AND THE COST OF DISEASE

Unfortunately there are no damage functions that could be used with the unit cost figures developed in this chapter to specify cost-of-pollution curves for health effects. Our attempts to develop such damage functions were not successful, as Appendix C shows. However, we can obtain a rough idea of the maximum extent to which air pollution is responsible for these estimated total losses by comparing urban and rural mortality rates corrected for as many nonpollution differences between urban and rural areas as possible. In 1949 the age-adjusted, white male mortality rates (per 100,000) for cancer of the lungs, emphysema, asthma, bronchitis, and bronchiectasis were 35.8 in urban and 23.8 in rural areas. On the basis of crude adjustments for smoking and age differences, plus different disease rates among women and nonwhites, approximately 20 per cent fewer deaths would result from these diseases if the adjusted rural rates applied to the urban population.[35] This figure is corroborated by calculations with

---

[35] From data provided by Emanuel Landau based on U. S.

data from a detailed study of lung cancer mortality rates in Pennsylvania, which were found to be 41 per cent higher for men and 21 per cent higher for women in urban as compared with rural areas after correcting for migration and differences in smoking and diagnosis. [36] With these figures properly weighted by population estimates in urban and rural areas of the U. S., and assuming the average mortality rate for lung cancer used in this study, the remaining urban-rural differences could account for 18 per cent of the total cases of this disease.

Since these figures are not corrected for occupational or more general socio-economic differences in urban and rural life, they indicate the maximum extent to which air pollution could be implicated. On the other hand, cardio-vascular diseases are more prevalent and cancer of the skin is less prevalent in urban than in rural areas, and there are some indications that they too are related to air pollution (cancer of the skin may be negatively related, since pollution reduces exposure to ultraviolet light, one of the causes of this disease). It is difficult to indicate in which direction these percentage estimates err due to these factors. But since the $2 billion figure for total cost is a substantial underestimate, we are probably still on the conservative side in attributing $360-400 million (18-20 per cent of $2 billion) to air pollution. Obviously, however, an adequate indication of health losses due to air pollution must await better epidemiological and laboratory data on the effects of pollution on human beings.

Public Health Service, Comparative Mortality Among Metropolitan Areas of the United States, 1949-1951 (Public Health Service Publication No. 562, October, 1957), and Vital Statistics of the United States, 1949.

[36]Hugh R. Gilmore and David M. Anderson, "Urban-Rural Differences in Lung Cancer Mortality Rates in the State," Pennsylvania Medical Journal, 66(2), February, 1963.

CHAPTER 4 SOILING AND MATERIALS-DAMAGE STUDIES

There is little doubt that air pollution can and has caused substantial losses due to soiling and deterioration of materials. Its role is well documented in experiments with test panels and experience gathered from major episodes. But estimates of the costs associated with materials damage due to normal levels of air pollution are very poor, and marginal cost estimates are virtually nonexistent.[1] Furthermore, nothing is known about how firms and households adjust -- whether, for example, they clean more frequently or more intensively, or simply suffer the additional dirt. This chapter reports on a number of attempts to develop such information in typical urban settings; the next chapter studies a special incident in which pollution levels rose far above normal for a short period.

In order to establish a cost curve or schedule, data must be found that indicate how the relevant costs vary over time or space with air pollution and with any other variables of at least equal explanatory importance. Because time-series data are generally too sparse for this purpose, it is necessary to rely on inter- and intra-urban cross-section materials.

---

[1]A good summary of what is known in this area is contained in John E. Yocom, "Effects of Air Pollution on Materials," Chapter 7A of Air Pollution, ed. Arthur C. Stern (New York: Academic Press, 1962), Vol. I, pp. 199-219

Some of these data are of such poor quality, and the ability to
control for the effects of other variables is so limited, that
one cannot expect to obtain good results. This evaluation is
amply illustrated by the studies presented below. However,
while they do not yield complete cost estimates, they are useful as a guide to what should and should not be done in the
future; and they strengthen the case for a proposal made at
the end of the chapter which, if adopted, would generate the
correct type of data for this purpose.

EVIDENCE FROM COMMERCE AND INDUSTRY

Interurban Studies of the Cleaning Service Industry

For many reasons, studies within urban areas can be expected to yield more adequate results than intercity studies.
The variation in air-pollution levels within an urban area is
quite large, so that it is not generally appropriate to represent the area by readings at one station; yet for most purposes
there is only one measurement station per city (and that in a
downtown location) which can be compared with those of other
cities. Furthermore, meteorological and topological conditions, which vary greatly among cities and cannot be easily or
successfully controlled for, can significantly reduce the re-
liability of the results. Nevertheless, the existence of data
from the National Air Sampling Network, and the inadequacy
of data on intracity receipts and expenditures, are strong in-
centives to attempt studies on this level. Those undertaken
as part of this study are briefly presented here to illustrate
and emphasize the problems with this approach.

Receipts of Laundry and Dry Cleaning Establishments

In an attempt to determine whether differences in air pollution can explain intercity variations in per capita expenditures
on laundry and dry cleaning services, information on the
annual receipts of different categories of firms supplying such
services was adjusted for population and compared with air-
pollution data for 144 cities throughout the United States.

Five standard categories of laundry and dry cleaning establishments were used: power laundries, family and commercial; self-service laundries; laundries, except power and
self-service; cleaning and dyeing plants, except rug cleaning;
and rug cleaning and repairing plants.[2] Establishments providing services primarily to industrial and commercial establishments (as well as diaper services) were not included. As
an index of soiling, measurements of suspended particulate
matter were relied upon, although perhaps one-fourth of the
tests were also tried using measures of benzene-soluble organic matter and sulfates.[3] Scatter diagrams comparing
suspended particulates with the combined benzene-soluble organic matter and suspended particulates suggest a sufficiently
high correlation that the former can be used as an index for
the others. To determine that the results were not influenced
by the measure of central tendency chosen, the tests were conducted using the arithmetic mean, the geometric mean, and the
80-th percentile. The main techniques of analysis were scatter
diagrams and rank correlation coefficients. Given the uniformly
negative findings, further analysis to obtain numerical estimates
of the relationships involved is not warranted.

Initially, the different categories of receipts per capita
were compared with the various measures of pollution. Since
no significant correlations emerged from this analysis, adjustments for other explanatory variables were attempted.

---

[2]Data from U. S. Census Bureau, 1958 Census of Business,
Selected Services, Vol. VI, Parts 1 and 2. Categories of establishments used were SIC groups 7211, 7215, 7212, 7216,
7217 and 7271pt.

[3]For most practical purposes these are the only comparable interurban air-pollution indexes available. Data on them
was taken from U. S. Department of Health, Education and
Welfare, Public Health Service, Air Pollution Measurements
of the National Air Sampling Network (Washington, D. C.:
U. S. Government Printing Office, 1962), Tables 2.3, 2.10,
and 2.20.

First, in an effort to control for the effects of climate, the sample was reduced and subdivided into three homogeneous climate zones. [4] Comparisons of receipts per capita and pollution indexes were then made within each zone. Second, both climate and income per capita were controlled[5] in a similar fashion; receipts per capita were plotted against pollution indexes for cities within subgroups based upon three categories of per capita income as well as climate zones. A third and final refinement was introduced by adjusting the per capita receipts for interurban price differentials. [6]

Altogether over thirty different comparisons between receipts and pollutants were developed. In none of them could any discernible pattern be detected in the data.

The Cost of Cleaning Office and Apartment Building Interiors

A picture similar to that for laundry and dry cleaning receipts emerges from data on the costs of cleaning office and apartment buildings. Through the help of Roy Wenzlick and

---

[4]The subdivisions were made on the basis of information obtained in G. T. Trewartha, A. H. Robinson, and E. H. Hammond, Fundamentals of Physical Geography (New York: McGraw-Hill, 1961), frontispiece map. The three climate zones used were (1) humid continental, cool summer (a subgroup of humid microthermal climates, (2) humid continental, warm summer (a subgroup of humid microthermal climates), and (3) humid subtropical, warm summer (a subgroup of humid mesothermal climates).

[5]Income and polulation data were obtained from U. S. Bureau of Census, 1960 Census Population, Vol. I (Washington, D. C.: U. S. Government Printing Office, 1961), Tables 30, 76, and 154.

[6]This adjustment used information on city workers' annual expenditures for "other goods and services," obtained from U. S. Department of Commerce, Bureau of the Census, Statistical Abstract of the U. S. , 1961 (Washington, D. C.: U. S. Government Printing Office, 1962), Table 456.

Company, St. Louis, Missouri, data were obtained on average costs of cleaning per square foot of office and apartment building space in a number of different cities throughout the United States. Since labor is the most important single component of these costs, and since significant differences in wages exist between cities, these average cost figures were deflated by an index of wages paid in the cleaning industry. To determine whether the remaining variation in cleaning costs could be explained by air pollution, correlations between these data and different measures of suspended particulates for the same cities were developed.

The results (with data sources) are given in Table 4 along with rank correlation coefficients showing the degree of association between deflated average cleaning costs and different pollution measures. These coefficients are uniformly low, indicating no association.[7] An attempt to control for differences in climate, using the method described above, did not improve the results.

Performance Frequencies by a Contract Cleaning Firm

It is possible that the foregoing data are too aggregated to detect the effects of air pollution. To partially test this explanation, the National Cleaning Contractors, Inc. agreed to request information from their branches in seven cities indicating the average, maximum, and minimum number of times per week or month that they performed specified cleaning chores under contract for their clients.[8] Altogether 85 differ-

---

[7]The rank correlation coefficients between undeflated cleaning costs and pollution are better. (For arithmetic means of particulates it is 0.41, for example.) This association, however, is spurious, since it is due to the fact that wages tend to be higher in industrial centers where pollution is also higher. (The rank correlation between wage rates and arithmetic means of particulates is 0.47).

[8]The cities, and their 1961 geometric means of suspended

Table 4

COMMERCIAL BUILDING INTERIOR CLEANING COSTS AND
SUSPENDED PARTICULATE MATTER, BY CITIES,
WITH RANK CORRELATION COEFFICIENTS

Cities	Annual Cleaning Costs Per Sq. Ft., $	Cleaning Industry Wage Index	Deflated Cleaning Costs, $	Suspended Particulate Matter (Micrograms per M^3, 1961)		
				Arith. Mean	Geom. Mean	90th Percentile
Chicago	62.20	189	32.90	190	179	254
New York City	70.00	172	40.70	173	167	241
Philadelphia	56.70	159	35.70	173	160	302
Milwaukee	37.30	148	25.20	146	135	234
Baltimore	45.80	120	38.20	142	132	180
St. Louis	50.60	137	36.90	141	132	214
Pittsburgh	67.70	161	42.00	137	126	214
Cleveland	42.30	148	28.60	136	126	214
Wash., D. C.	45.10	117	38.50	128	112	214
Detroit	82.40	168	49.00	118	110	173
Dallas	40.70	105	38.80	92	84	145
Seattle	49.20	187	26.30	87	76	151
Atlanta	47.10	100	47.10	84	78	122
Miami	33.50	133	25.18	54	52	76
Rank Correlation Coefficient				-0.06	-0.03	-0.10

Sources: Cost information from National Association of Building Owners and Managers, Forty-third Annual Experience Exchange Report, Office Building Operations Calendar Year 1962 (Chicago: 1963) and Institute of Real Estate Management of the National Association of Real Estate Boards, Apartment Building Experience Exchange of Rental Income and Operating Expense Data, special issue of Journal of Property Management (Chicago: 1963). Wage index computed from average wage data provided in "Earnings in Contract Cleaning Services Summer 1961," Monthly Labor Review, Vol. 85, Jan.-June 1962, pp. 402-404. Data on suspended particulates from U.S. Department of Health, Education and Welfare, Public Health Service, Air Pollution Measurements of the National Air Sampling Network (Washington, D. C.: U.S. Government Printing Office, 1962), Table 2.3.

ent chores were reported on, ranging from the dusting of fix-
tures and window sills to the shampooing of carpets.

Except for two tasks in one city, all chores were performed
with identical average, maximum, and minimum frequencies in
all seven cities. Thus, for example, windows are cleaned inside and out on an average of once every five weeks (with the
maximum and minimum frequencies being once every four
weeks and once every two months), no matter what city was
reported and venetian blinds and window frames are dusted
once every two months (the maximum and minimum figures
being once per month and once per year) in each city.

Assuming these frequencies are correct and typical, their
explanation is likely to involve three principal considerations.
Perhaps most important is the likelihood that variations in air-
pollution components causing soiling are probably not great
enough relative to other explanatory variables to cause observable variations in cleaning behavior. Although the data indicate over a two-fold difference between the lowest and the
highest values for suspended particulates in these cities, this
difference may still not be enough to be noticeable in the light
of similarities in custom, desire for uniformity, ability to pay,
and similar variables that could not be controlled for. Closely
related to this explanation is the phenomenon of judging cleanliness by the frequency of cleaning. Since it takes a large
variation in levels of cleanliness to be noticed and since the
product being sold is not cleanliness but a certain number of
cleanings per time period, it is quite understandable that emphasis might be placed upon frequencies of cleaning rather
than need. Another explanation is that most modern buildings
are more or less sealed from the outside atmosphere so that

------

particulates, are: New York City (167), Newark (99), Philadelphia (160), Hartford (72), Chicago (179), St. Louis (132)
and Los Angeles (154).

differences in <u>internal</u> pollution and dirt levels between buildings in different cities may not be detectable, no matter what
the outside differences might be. [9] These explanations tend to
be corroborated by the findings of the intra-urban studies, to
which we now turn.

Intra-urban Studies

There are virtually no published data available on areas
within a city that can help determine the soiling costs of air
pollution. However, with the cooperation of a number of business firms in St. Louis, some evidence on this subject was
generated.

Supermarket Sales of Cleaning Supplies

One piece of evidence for pollution-induced cleaning expenditures by householders is the purchase of cleaning supplies.
Data on such purchases are obtainable from either side of the
market -- from the householders themselves or from the
stores that sell to them. Since there are many more buyers
than sellers, it is far easier and cheaper to obtain the data
from the sellers -- if they will cooperate. However, this approach has a number of sufficiently serious disadvantages [10]

----

[9]This explanation does not account for identical frequencies
for external cleanings. But the only chores listed that pertain
to the outside are window washings and cleaning of doors and
entrance passages. The other explanations are likely to apply to these tasks.

[10]Such data can at best indicate only one of the ways that
householders may adjust to soiling caused by pollution. Instead of increasing market purchases, persons living in dirtier areas may simply put up with the additional soiling, or
may spend more time and energy, instead of money, in cleaning. Evidence on such alternative ways of adjusting can only
be obtained by direct questionnaires. Furthermore, to com-
bine data from sellers with air-pollution information, it is
necessary to make an assumption about the area within which

that no more than an exploratory effort to apply it was undertaken. The larger supermarket chains were asked to provide
data on sales of cleaning supplies as a per cent of total sales
by individual stores. Only one chain, the Bettendorf-Rapp
Company, was willing to provide such information. Their
data were combined with air-pollution data, on the assumption that most of their customers came from within a two-
mile radius of each store. No pattern is discernible in these
data, even when rough adjustments for income per capita in
different parts of the metropolitan area are introduced.

Maintenance Procedures

Another possible source of evidence is the cleaning and
maintenance procedures followed by business firms with operations in different parts of the city. To obtain such information persons responsible for cleaning and maintenance in two
chains of department stores, two supermarket chains, two
chains of drive-in restaurants, and one public utility were interviewed. The following generalizations can be drawn from
the evidence that was gathered.

First, most cleaning and maintenance procedures are
undertaken on a schedule that does not vary with the location
of the operation. Display windows are washed weekly, street
lights yearly, delivery trucks monthly, and so on. The most
important reason for this pattern of behavior is simply that
differences in soiling in different parts of the city do not make

---

the customers of a particular store live. This can be done
with reasonable accuracy for some stores such as supermarkets, which draw customers from a limited radius around
the store, but not for department and hardware stores which
also sell cleaning supplies. If, however, the study is limited
to supermarkets, only one part of household expenditures on
cleaning supplies is being obtained. Finally, it is difficult to
control for other variables, such as income and standards of
cleanliness, that could also explain differences in purchases
of cleaning supplies.

a sufficient, observable difference to warrant the inconvenience of not following uniform procedures. [11]

Second, even when no deliberate effort is made to maintain uniformity, no association between soiling costs and air pollution was generally found; and factors other than air pollution appear to be more important in explaining the cleaning and maintenance procedures. The type of parking lots (dirt, stone or paved) around a store are more important than general air-pollution levels in determining the amount of dirt tracked into a store; and the cleaning problems resulting therefrom depend primarily on the type of floor covering. The frequency with which air-conditioning filters are changed depends upon the type of air-conditioning units and filters used, which typically differs even among stores of the same company. In any case, most air conditioners recycle internal air, which results in filters becoming dirty primarily from lint and dust from clothing. The soiling of merchandise in department stores depends primarily upon the extent to which buildings are sealed against dirt from the outside and the extent to which merchandise is handled (which in part depends upon how it is displayed). [12] The fading of dyes in merchandise in display windows depends upon the degree to which overhanging roofs and tinted glass protect it from sunlight (in any case, to the extent that pollution obscures the sun, it should reduce fading). None of these factors could be controlled for to determine whether remaining differences in cleaning and maintenance costs could be caused by air pollution.

---

[11] Uniform procedures are more convenient in that administrative supervision and scheduling of work are simplified. But, if firms believed that differences in soiling were important, they would surely give up some of these conveniences.

[12] Downtown stores sometimes report more soiling losses than suburban stores, but this could easily be explained by the fact that they are typically much older and less well protected from outside dirt and dust.

Third, the only reference to problems caused by air pollution was the fly ash that collects on ledges and cooling towers, particularly in downtown locations. This is more a matter of annoyance than anything else, and no indications of the cost that such pollution might entail could be obtained.

Materials-Damage Studies

Similar findings result from investigating the relationship between air pollution and expenditures to avoid or replace materials damaged by air pollution. To find adequate data for a statistical analysis of these relationships is even more difficult than for those in the foregoing discussion. Since the time periods between such expenditures are generally much longer than in the case of soiling, it is more difficult to obtain adequate records and there are more intervening variables to contend with. To illustrate these findings we present one case study and the results of a series of interviews with knowledgeable persons in different industries faced with pollution problems.

Maintenance of Electric Transmission Towers

The Union Electric Company of St. Louis has over 1, 800 electric towers scattered throughout the St. Louis metropolitan area that have, in their lifetimes, been painted more than once. Since maintenance personnel of this company indicated that these towers are repainted when inspection indicates it is "necessary" rather than on a set schedule, a unique opportunity is provided to determine whether an association is present between the frequency of repaintings -- which can easily be transformed into a cost figure -- and the detailed air-pollution measurements available for St. Louis.

The company provided detailed records indicating the date of installation, the dates of painting, and the number and approximate location of towers throughout the city. Information on location is only approximate in some cases because the maintenance records are grouped by transmission lines of varying lengths and numbers of towers. This material was

compared with information on pollution levels derived from
isopleth maps of sulfation levels and suspended particulates
and from individual station readings for dustfall measurements.
The results of these comparisons are presented in Figure 2 .
In some cases, lines rather than points had to be plotted to
account for the fact that many transmission lines cut across
several pollution zones. Code letters and the numbers of towers for each line are indicated beside each point or line segment. [13]

For all practical purposes, the findings are negative. This
is certainly the case when frequencies are plotted against sulfation and suspended particulate measurements (although it is
possible that had information on mean pollution levels for
each line been available a better fit would have been obtained).
So far as dustfall is concerned, a reasonable plot through the
data can be drawn; but this is risky because dustfall measurements are relevant only within a few hundred yards of each
station, and only a few stations fall within reasonable distances
of the transmission lines. [14]

---

[13]In addition to the three plots indicated, a fourth was
tried using as a pollution index the product of the sulfation and
dustfall measurements. While this involves an arbitrary
weighting, it represents a simple way to investigate the possibility that the combination of both pollutants is more important than either one. No association was found.

[14]This diagram can be used, however, as an illustration of
how a cost-of-pollution curve can be obtained from a damage
function. It costs approximately $300 to paint a tower, accord-
ing to Union Electric. If one fitted a curve to the observed
data (as illustrated in Figure 2), read frequencies for given
dustfall levels from this curve, divided each such frequency
into $300 and replotted the results against the dustfall measure-
ments, a curve that looks very similar to the cost-of-pollution
curve presented in Figure 1 of Chapter 1 would be obtained.

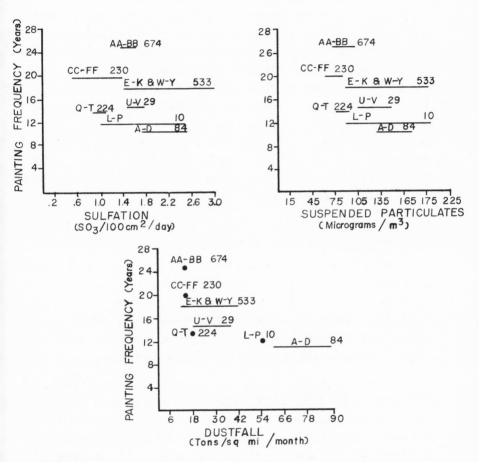

Figure 2
FREQUENCY OF ELECTRIC TRANSMISSION TOWER
PAINTING VS. AIR POLLUTION
St. Louis, Mo. 1912-64[a]

[a]Letters indicate the symbols used to identify the lines included in each observation. Numbers after the letters indicate the number of towers included in each observation. Observations indicated by horizontal lines indicate that the towers involved fell into more than one pollution zone.

Source: Drawn from information supplied by Union Electric Company on transmission tower painting frequency and isopleths appearing in Jack R. Farmer, "Interstate Air Pollution Study Air Quality Measurements February 1965" (mimeo, Interstate Air Pollution Study, St Louis, Missouri).

Perhaps the most important explanation of this finding is that the tower installation and repainting history starts in 1912 with the smallest gap between paintings being eleven years. Current readings on air pollution are unlikely to be representative of the pollution levels that caused the need for repainting in the past. In addition, the company faced a variety of budgetary constraints (such as the depression of the 1930's); there have been changes in metal and paint technology; and inspection standards may have changed considerably. Such factors could cause substantial changes in maintenance procedures, even if relative levels of air pollution between observations had remained constant over this period. Whatever the case may be, clearly there is no simple causal link between the presence of sulfation, dustfall, and suspended particulates on the one hand and frequency of repainting on the other.

Experience of Industrial Firms

A search for similar sources of data that might be associated with air pollution uncovered none that were free of problems involved in the above case study. However, in the process, interviews and correspondence with a variety of industrial establishments brought to light additional qualitative information which should be of some interest.

The Southwest Bell Telephone Company and Union Electric Company, both of St. Louis, provided some evidence on problems they have had with equipment in various parts of the city. The contamination of insulators by dirt causes flashovers that interrupt service and sometimes cause electric-line pole fires. But weather patterns, the voltage carried, and the circuitry configuration play such overriding roles that no locational problems related to air pollution can be identified.[15] Strand,

[15]Furthermore, no cost estimates are kept by this category so that it is not known how much is spent cleaning insulators or repairing pole-fire damage, or what such fires cost customers whose service is interrupted.

guy wire, and the like normally deteriorate so slowly over time -- normally in 30 or 40 years except where steam locomotives are still used and sometimes near chemical plants -- that differences due to general urban pollution levels cannot be observed. In earlier years, before the introduction of smoke ordinances and while malleable iron was still used, serious corrosion problems appear to have been present (although there are no numerical records to corroborate this impression). However, the shift from malleable iron to galvanized steel and from metals to plastics -- which was undertaken for a variety of reasons, among them the fact that the plastics became cheaper -- appears to have brought the corrosion problem down to the point where it is not noticeable except in extreme environments.

Manufacturers of computers and electronic equipment[16] indicated that the reduction or elimination of normal types of urban air pollution would not affect the way in which they make their equipment, nor the normal maintenance procedures performed. The biggest maintenance problems faced, apparently, are associated with the need to protect the equipment from changes in humidity and temperature; voltage variations; chemicals emitted from some lubricants, gaskets, seals, and plastics; customer-generated pollutants (for example, in oil refineries and electroplating shops); and sometimes soiling caused by the presence of Coca-Cola, coffee, and ashes from cigarettes. One firm indicated a belief that their costs must be higher due to air pollution, but could offer no examples of cases where they were.

Steel-producing and -fabricating companies[17] indicated

---

[16]Monroe Business Machines, Westinghouse Electric, International Business Machines, Minneapolis Honeywell, and Radio Corporation of America.

[17]United States Steel, Kaiser Steel, Republic Steel, and Jones and Laughlin Steel Corporation.

that pollution undoubtedly affects their products but that corro-sion-resistant compounds are marketed for other reasons as well (for example, for use in food processing). They could not identify the differential costs attributable solely to air pollution. U. S. Steel did indicate that a new product, Cor-Ten Steel, which requires no protective coating in normal applications, sells for $60 per ton more than normal carbon steels; but this product is too new to know how much will be used in different applications.

The Steel Structures Painting Council, Pittsburgh, estima-ted that roughly $500 million is spent per year in applying corrosion-inhibiting coatings to metal surfaces. However, most steel is painted primarily for appearance, and probably less than 5 per cent is in locations where high levels of ag-gressive chemical pollutants require more frequent repaint-ings. Presumably, differences in more normal levels of urban pollution do not result in noticeable differences in steel-painting frequencies or practices. As for other uses of paint, major paint companies[18] indicated that most modern paints are not seriously affected by urban air pollutants, that these paints would be in general use even in the absence of such pollution, and that in special situations where pollution is ex-pected to be a problem they can substitute alternative pigment bases at no extra cost to the user.

The general impression derived from these sources is that air pollution undoubtedly makes a difference -- it would be hard to imagine that it does not -- but that there is not enough information to say exactly what the difference is.

---

[18]Benjamin Moore Paint Company, Glidden, National Lead, and Pittsburgh Plate Glass Company.

EVIDENCE FROM HOUSEHOLDS

There are virtually no published materials that are useful in obtaining a direct estimate of the costs incurred by households due to air pollution. These costs will only be revealed by data gathered specifically for this purpose. Only then is there a chance to observe the different forms in which these costs may occur and to control for all the other variables besides air pollution that influence these costs. This section summarizes the results of a study that attempted to gather such information. [19]

More specifically, the primary purpose of this study was to develop a questionnaire that would assess the extent to which cleaning and maintenance costs in the home are related to air pollution. To test the questionnaire, personal interviews were conducted with some six hundred housewives equally divided among three different areas of Philadelphia. [20] These areas were selected so that their differences with respect to

---

[19] The Philadelphia division of Daniel Yankelovich, Inc. was engaged to develop, implement, and analyze the questionnaire on the basis of guidelines given to them.

[20] It may be of interest to compare the methods and results of this study with the only other study that we know of that comes close to using the same procedures. This study is presented in an unpublished report, "The Economic Cost of Air Pollution -- ARF Project No. 9-851, " conducted by the Armour Research Foundation (now Illinois Institute of Technology) in 1960 for the Consumers Union, Inc. While it comes to definite numerical conclusions, these results are questionable on a number of grounds, principally the facts that a mail questionnaire was used and that controls for nonpollution factors that could also explain the observed differences in costs were far from adequate. See also Irving Michelson and Boris Tourin, "Comparative Method for Studying Costs of Air Pollution, " Public Health Reports, Vol. 81, No. 6, June, 1966, pp. 505-11 and references given therein.

air pollution would be maximized and all other differences
minimized. While this procedure fails to yield a representative sample of the metropolitan area, it maximizes the chances
of obtaining significant relationships between the dependent
variables of this study and air pollution.

Even though areas were deliberately chosen in this way,
the results of the study are largely negative. For this reason,
and because a detailed report is available elsewhere,[21] this
discussion is limited to a general description of the study and
its broader conclusions. These conclusions and the reasons
for the negative findings are important, for they have a bearing on the approach to this problem that should be used in the
future.

Study Design

The sample sites were selected after investigation of census materials and air-pollution data for seven different cities.
Some sites were ruled out because adequate data were lacking,
others because of insufficient differences in pollution levels,
and still others because of excessive correlation between pollution levels and socio-economic indicators such as race, income, and occupation. The final choice of sites, selected
with the help and advice of the Air Pollution Control Section of
the Philadelphia Department of Public Health,[22] is a compromise among these criteria.

On the surface, the areas are remarkably similar. The
houses are practically all two-story, brick row houses, close

----

[21]A detailed report on methods and statistical findings is
contained in the final report by Yankelovich, Inc. It is on
file with the Division of Air Pollution, U.S. Public Health
Service, as are all the data gathered in this study.

[22]We are indebted to Lawrence Himmelstein, Assistant
Chief of that Section, for the data, time, and advice he provided us.

to the street and roughly comparable in size and condition. Census data indicated considerable similarity in household composition, educational and occupational composition, and income. Similarities between the samples were increased by selecting only white housewives as respondents. Upon analysis of the questionnaires larger differences in potentially important variables such as income and ethnic background were found, but these differences are considerably less than would have been found in randomly selected census tracts and could be controlled for in the statistical analysis.

On the other hand, differences in suspended and settled dust in two of these sample areas are sufficiently great to be observed by the naked eye. The third area fell between the first two on these scales, but after field work was completed, revised pollution data were made available indicating that sulfation levels were higher there than in the other two areas. While the settled and suspended dust should be most important for our purposes, this discrepancy may account for some of the unexpected responses obtained from this area. In view of the negative findings of this survey, a discussion of these discrepant results from the third area is unnecessary, and they are not dealt with further here. Table 5 presents information on the levels of air pollution in the two extreme areas.

To develop the questionnaire, a series of open-ended group and individual depth interviews were undertaken in the high- and low-pollution areas. The purposes of these interviews were to determine the specific categories of cleaning and maintenance costs of particular relevance to persons in these areas and to anticipate problems and areas of resistance that might be encountered in more structured interviews. The questionnaire developed from this material was pretested and modified in several rounds until the final form, presented in Appendix D, emerged. This final questionnaire represents a compromise between the amount of detail and cross-checks for accuracy initially desired and what housewives appeared able and willing to answer in a period of one hour.[23]

For the final survey, straight random samples of individual housing units were drawn from each of the sample areas. Interviewers were instructed to choose only white, female household residents who play a major role in the cleaning, laundering,and maintenance activities of the housing unit. Two call-backs were required before substituting another address. Because of an unexpectedly high rate of ineligibility and nonresponse, and the small size of the sample areas, the resulting samples are close to a complete census of the available and eligible households in each area. Interviewers were rotated between the sample areas to avoid biases that might otherwise result.

TABLE 5

AIR-POLLUTION INDEXES FOR SAMPLE AREAS

Index	Monthly Average Value, 1960–65	
	High-Pollution Area	Low-Pollution Area
Suspended Dust [a]	167	104
Settled Dust [b]	54. 1	28. 2
Sulfates [c]	2. 30	1. 83

[a] Micrograms per cubic meter.
[b] Tons per square mile per month.
[c] Micrograms of SO_3 per square mile per day.
Source: Air Pollution Control Section of Philadelphia Division of Public Health.

---

[23] As a consequence, some of the ways in which costs might occur, for example in increased intensity of activity, had to be left out.

Analysis and Results

The dependent variables of this study fall roughly into eight categories:

(1) Frequency of outside painting and inside papering and painting (questions 23 and 24).

(2) Time spent in routine cleaning (questions 25-28).

(3) Hours of use of selected garments between cleaning (questions 39 and 40).

(4) Expenditures on cleaning and laundering supplies (questions 31, 42, and 45).

(5) Frequency of washing cars (question 47).

(6) Willingness to pay for amelioration of the problem (questions 63-66).

(7) Property and rental values (questions 77 and 78).[24]

(8) Questions that permit the respondent to indicate other influences and concerns with the problem of air pollution (questions 1-6, 18, 50-57 and 60-62).

Table 6 presents summary data for responses to a selected group of items in categories 1, 2, and 4. An outline of the principal independent variables which in addition to air pollution might also explain the observed differences in responses to the dependent variables is presented in Table 7.

The analysis of this material took three forms: first, a review of the completed interview schedules; second, a study of tables in which summary statistics for each response (and some groups of responses) were classified by air-pollution zones; and finally, multiple-regression analysis of three sets

---

[24]While property and rental values are dependent variables in the sense that they are affected by air pollution, they are also independent variables in that they may have an effect on cleaning and maintenance expenditures independently of air pollution. For this reason, information on them is included in Table 7.

Table 6

SELECTED RESPONSES TO CLEANING AND MAINTENANCE QUESTIONS
BY SAMPLE AREAS

Cleaning and Maintenance Activities and Associated Units	High-Pollution Area			Low-Pollution Area			P^a
	Mean	Variance	Number Responding	Mean	Variance	Number Responding	
Months between Performance							
Paint Outside Woodwork	59.0	2798.7	176	53.2	1563.7	163	.750
Paint Living Room Woodwork	65.4	6518.3	185	64.7	1828.8	185	.080
Paint Living Room Walls	46.2	673.5	39	66.5	11499.1	83	.895
Paper Living Room Walls	81.0	5448.1	155	80.4	2260.3	117	.063
Minutes per Month							
Wash Windows Outside	97.3	8367.7	194	83.2	5865.6	188	.899
Wash Windows Inside	258.4	21022.9	195	265.0	17704.1	192	.376
Dust Sills Outside	226.4	26296.9	181	198.7	18452.2	182	.922
Dust Sills Inside	330.8	45952.4	197	432.1	45546.5	195	.999
Wash or Clean Front Door	291.0	26373.1	168	279.1	33348.6	175	.578
Vacuum Living Room Rug	412.3	63914.7	164	462.8	65852.2	187	.937
Dust Living Room Woodwork	363.3	43932.1	195	383.6	39008.4	195	.678
Cents per Month							
Laundry Detergent	218.0	21516.7	191	239.4	34759.1	194	.789
Liquid All-Purpose Cleaner	121.7	8781.4	131	86.3	3534.8	153	.452
Floor Wax	76.5	5487.3	115	67.7	3764.0	126	.111
Window Cleaner	49.8	2781.7	118	46.4	1899.8	140	.425

[a] P is the probability that the observed difference in Means is statistically significant, that is, not due to chance.

78

Table 7

SELECTED INDEPENDENT VARIABLES BY SAMPLE AREAS

Independent Variable	High-Pollution Area (N=198)[a]	Low-Pollution Area (N=196)[a]
Housing		
Brick or Stone	99.0%	96.0%
Number of Rooms	6.1	7.0
Number of Windows	11.2	14.8
Have Air Conditioning	30.3%	41.0%
Heating System - Fuel		
Coal	15.2%	2.0%
Gas	52.0%	54.6%
Oil	32.8%	43.4%
Heating System - Delivery		
Hot Air	48.0%	15.8%
Occupants		
Number Persons	3.4	3.7
Age of Female Head	47	47
Ethnic Origin - Italian	8.2%	77.9%
Irish	22.6%	10.8%
Polish	33.3%	0.5%
Residence Less Than 5 Years	28.8%	25.5%
One or More Dogs in House	30.8%	14.8%
One or More Cats in House	7.1%	5.6%
Economic Characteristics		
Income	$6,090	$8,140
Home Ownership	77.8%	81.3%
Property Value (Owner Occupied)	$6,990	$11,870
Rent (Renter Occupied)	$54	$73
Occupation Male Head		
White Collar[b]	10.1%	16.2%
Blue Collar[b]	67.9%	61.8%
Employed Female Head		
Full Time	16.3%	11.7%
Part Time	2.5%	6.7%
Use Domestic Help	4.0%	14.0%
Education Female Head		
Less Than High School	70.3%	58.6%
High School Graduate[c]	26.9%	36.6%
Smoking		
Households with Smokers	73.0%	75.0%
Number of Cigarettes	25.4	21.9
Subjective Cleanliness Standards[d]		
Cleanliness Most Important	25.0%	36.0%
Cleanliness Fairly Important	45.0%	41.0%
Cleanliness Is Secondary	28.0%	23.0%

[a]Percentage figures are percentage of number responding to the question. In most cases the number responding is the same as, or very close to, the sample size, N. The only important exception is for income where responses were 160 and 159 in the two areas.

[b]Those who are not white or blue collar are part-time or retired.

[c]High school graduate means exactly 12 years, no more. Those not in the two categories specified have more than 12 years of schooling.

[d]See question 29 of questionnaire for wording. Ethnic origin may also give clues to standards.

of dependent variables. [25] The results are uniformly so poor
that only a brief summary is required to characterize them.

The completed interview schedules, plus comments from
the interviewers, suggest that many of the responses to behavioral questions are unreliable indicators of actual behavior.
Many women apparently answered to be obliging or to make a
good impression. Table 6 is typical of the cross-classification
tables for questions referring to cleaning and maintenance behavior. Some of the means are suspiciously high; differences
between mean responses in the high- and low-pollution areas
are sometimes positive, sometimes negative, and most times
insignificant; and intrasample variances are generally very
large. The multiple-regression analysis confirms this picture.
This analysis was undertaken to determine if the means and
variances adjusted for the effects of the independent variables
would present a different and hopefully more reliable picture.
They do not. Even when some fourteen independent variables
are included, the best of the equations explains only 8 per
cent of the variance in the dependent variable. Given the relatively large number of independent variables and observations involved, this result must be considered quite significant:
the correlation between the dependent and independent variables, including air pollution, is virtually zero.

The only questions that appear to distinguish between the
sampling areas in the expected way are the willingness-to-pay

---

[25]The sets of dependent variables were time spent in routine cleaning outside, time spent in routine cleaning inside,
and the sum of these two. Some fourteen independent variables were permitted to enter the regression equations, one at
a time in order of importance. These included three measures
of air pollution (in some runs a dummy variable for the sample area was included in place of these measures), household
income, number of persons in household, age and ethnic origin of female head, indications of housekeeping standards,
and types of heating systems.

and the attitude questions. Table 8 summarizes responses to
the willingness-to-pay questions. When asked in open-ended
questions about disadvantages of their neighborhood relative
to others in the city, 15 per cent mentioned odors or soot in the
dirtier area as opposed to 2 per cent in the cleaner area.
When asked whether they would like to see more tax dollars
spent on pollution control as opposed to other metropolitan
services (question 50), 23 per cent responded affirmatively
in the high-pollution and 20 per cent in the low-pollution area.
On the other hand, 6 per cent in the dirtier area (10 per cent
in the cleaner area) indicated that an advantage of their neighborhood is its cleanliness. There appears to be a small group
in each of the areas that is concerned with air pollution and
the larger of the groups resides in the dirtier area. For the
overwhelming majority, however, air pollution and the cleaning and maintenance costs it may cause do not loom large.

Interpretation of Results

Should we conclude from this evidence that, at least for the
observations used in this study, air pollution does not affect
cleaning and maintenance costs in the home? Or should we
conclude that the methods applied to measure those costs were
not adequate? The next chapter presents a case study in which
pollution levels rose far above normal for a short time. While
that study is subject to some of the same difficulties as this
one, at least some numerical results are obtained even though
the questionnaire is much cruder than this one. This suggests
either that the differences in pollution levels in the Philadelphia
sample areas are not great enough to affect cleaning and maintenance costs or that people in the dirtier area have adjusted to
these costs not by cleaning more often but by bearing more
psychic costs. Undoubtedly an even larger difference in pollution levels would have increased the likelihood of observing a
significant cost difference; and the higher figures for willingness-
to-pay in the dirtier area could be used to suggest higher psychic costs. But the large intrasample variances, the inability
to reduce them by controlling for the effects of nonpollution

Table 8

WILLINGNESS-TO-PAY PER MONTH
FOR POLLUTION CONTROL

Type of Solution	High-Pollution Area			Low-Pollution Area			
	Mean	Variance	No.[a] of Responses	Mean	Variance	No.[a] of Responses	P[b]
Complete Solution[c]	$0.62	$0.43	143	$0.43	$0.07	64	.80
Private Solution[d]	0.55	0.37	142	0.45	0.15	64	.80
Neighborhood Solution[e]	0.62	0.28	143	0.46	0.25	64	.95

[a] For the most part nonresponses indicate a belief that the air is clean rather than an inability or unwillingness to answer the questions. The instructions after question 56 indicate that the persons with such a belief were not asked the willingness-to-pay questions. Presumably, they would have been willing to pay nothing, and the mean responses should be adjusted downward accordingly.

[b] P is the probability that the observed difference in means is significant, that is, not due to chance.

[c] Question 63 of questionnaire.
[d] Question 65 of questionnaire.
[e] Question 66 of questionnaire.

independent variables, and the qualitative arguments given below raise doubts as to the accuracy of this questionnaire as a measurement device.

The principal weakness of the questionnaire lies in its assumption that a housewife's _actual_ behavior corresponds closely to her behavior as she _perceives_ it. There are many reasons why this correspondence is weak. Cleaning can almost be described as a spare-time activity in the sense that almost anything can interrupt it -- a call or visit from a friend, a headache, or a sick child. The time it takes is probably governed by the time available for it, which varies from day to day. Nor is it a task that occupies much conscious thought. Questions about the average duration and frequency of certain tasks, therefore, are likely to come as a surprise and may not even have any meaning for the housewife. In this situation the answers cannot be trusted. Some women will answer in terms of goals, others in terms of a personal time system which depends upon mood or necessities of the moment, and still others more or less accurately. Individual personality differences are probably more important than income, age, or ethnic background in explaining these differences.

These considerations throw doubts on the validity of responses to some of the other questions as well. If responses to questions about simple, routine tasks cannot be trusted, responses about relatively rare tasks where memory plays a larger role must also include substantial errors. If recently past behavior cannot be accurately reported, statements about likely future behavior cannot be given much credence. Responses to the willingness-to-pay questions are probably useful as expressions of concern but certainly not as indications of likely future behavior. Indeed, responses to open-ended questions suggest that only a small number understood what their "willingness-to-pay" might purchase for them. Similar arguments can be applied to questions that attempt to measure housekeeping standards and income.

While many of these problems were recognized at the outset, they proved to be more critical than anticipated. It now
seems evident that a much narrower, deeper, and psychologically sophisticated questionnaire is required to measure and
untangle the various determinants of cleaning costs. Such a
questionnaire would require substantially more time and ex-
expenditure -- perhaps three to four times greater -- than
went into this essentially exploratory study. Even then the
probability of success may not be very high, for such a project would raise problems in survey design that have not yet
been solved.

A Proposal

In addition to the special problems with the household survey there are several other possible explanations for the negative findings discussed in this chapter. First, air pollution
at normally experienced levels may simply not be an important factor in accounting for the costs of the soiling and
deterioration of materials. Second, measurements of air
pollution, as well as other variables, may be too inaccurate
for the purpose. Third, the measurements available may not
be appropriate; that is, some other measures of central tendency or groups of pollutants should be used. Or, fourth, there
may be too many intervening variables whose effects could
not be held constant in order to observe the independent effect
of air pollution.

The first explanation is far from being proved -- or dis-
proved -- by the data presented here. If it were correct, the
bulk of the observations in a scatter diagram would have fallen
near a horizontal line indicating that the costs involved are the
same regardless of the level of pollution. Instead, such diagrams indicate no association whatsoever. This result, plus
the qualitative evidence presented, strongly suggests that the
fourth explanation is important. Unfortunately, our findings
shed very little light on the other possibilities, which are just
as plausible.

There is no reason to believe that additional studies relying on currently available data are suddenly going to yield positive results, or that they would even reveal where the difficulty lies. Gathering new data by use of sample surveys is costly, and under the best of circumstances the percentage of unexplained variance is likely to be high. For these reasons I propose, as an alternative that should work in a number of areas where other methods fail, a special type of experimental approach to the gathering of the relevant economic information.

The typical experimental approach used with materials is to place panels of pure uncoated metal, paint, or cloth in exposed locations where air-pollution measurements are also available. Observations over time of the extent of the deterioration are quite useful in establishing an index of the corrosiveness of the environment. They can also be used in conjunction with data on air pollution and weather conditions to establish an equation that will explain or predict the amount of deterioration resulting from specified exposure conditions. A good example along these lines is the following equation developed by Sereda:[26]

$$Y = 0.131 X + 0.0180 Z + 0.787,$$

where

Y = log of corrosion rate (mg per sq dm per day of wetness),
X = sulfur dioxide pollution rate (mg sulfur trioxide per sq dm per day),
Z = temperature in Farenheit (monthly average during the time-of-wetness).

A similar equation for the loss of leaves from certain plants as a result of exposure to SO_3 has been developed by observing plants in laboratory experiments.

---

[26]P. J. Sereda, "Atmospheric Factors Affecting the Corrosion of Steel," Industrial and Engineering Chemistry, Vol. 2, Feb.,1960, pp. 157-60.

However valuable they may be for other purposes, such
equations are not useful in establishing the economic cost of
deterioration. Pure, uncoated metals are not objects of
common use in the economy. Cloth is not stretched tautly on
a frame in normal uses. Paint, cloth, and metals are seldom,
if ever, exposed to as hostile an environment as that utilized
in the experimental situation. Clothing spends much of its
useful life in drawers; and perhaps half of all paint is used on
surfaces on the inside of buildings, and even that used exter-
nally is protected somewhat by overhanging roofs and is typically on vertical rather than horizontal surfaces. Furthermore, the weight of corrosive compounds on the surface of
metals, the loss of fiber strength in fabrics, physical measure
ments of changes in the color of dyes and pigments, and the
reduction in reflected light intensity as an index of soiling are
seldom adequate even as proxies for losses of economic
function. [27] What is needed for economic studies are experimental data derived from observations on economic objects in
conditions corresponding closely to actual use, and measurements on these objects of either the direct loss in economic
function or the loss incurred to avoid or offset such direct
losses.

The experiment would have to be designed to accommodate
the peculiarities of the specific case being considered. Thus,
the most reliable method for estimating the costs of maintain-
ing painted exterior surfaces is likely to involve locating small
scale models[28] of freshly painted exterior surfaces of

---

[27]At least these indexes cannot be assumed adequate for
economic studies before the hypothesis is tested. Apparently,
for certain plants, leaf loss and loss of yield have been found
to be highly correlated. But such a situation may be unique.

[28]A sufficient model for this case might be a cubic struc-
ture one to two square feet on a side, made of typical exterior building materials and protected by a roof with a slight
overhang, and painted on each side with a typical quality and
color of exterior paint.

buildings at each air-pollution measurement station throughout
a metropolitan area. The models would be inspected periodically to determine when they compare unfavorably with certain
standards of taste indicating the stage of soiling or deterioration at which the model should be repainted. Standards could
be chosen by showing samples of painted surfaces at different
degrees of deterioration to a representative panel and asking
whether, if their building looked like the sample, they would
repaint. Such an experiment would produce a set of observations from which a curve could be drawn describing, for any
given level of tastes, the relationship between paintings per
time period and the level of air pollution. Other levels of
taste would produce similar curves which, hopefully, would
have similar shapes but which in any case, if appropriately
weighted, could be combined into one curve. Supplementary
studies could be used to estimate the typical cost of repainting
and the extent of the painted exterior surfaces in each pollution zone. A curve similar to the cost-of-pollution curve illustrated in Figure 1 of Chapter 1 (or an equation similar to
the one presented above except that the dependent variable
would be cost of painting per time period) could then easily be
generated from this data. The same method could be used to
obtain cost functions for a variety of soiling problems as well
as some cases of materials damage.

If pollution measurement stations could be set up wherever
desired, it would be possible to use existing structures instead of models, and in some cases this would significantly
shorten the time required to obtain the evidence. For this
purpose records would have to be obtained showing when particular buildings were last painted and what quality of paint
was used. The standard samples would then be used to determine whether the buildings in the sample needed painting
(given each standard); and for those buildings not requiring
painting at the time of inspection, either a projection of the
date when it will be needed or later inspections would be
required. [29]

---

[29]Something like this procedure is probably required in

If the time interval between maintenance or repair is too long to permit other approaches to be used, laboratory simulation of the same conditions might be considered. While many technical problems would have to be solved, it might in the long run be the least expensive approach for many categories of damage. In principle, levels of air pollution could be varied at will and the deterioration or soiling process speeded up so that a great deal of evidence could be obtained without duplication of equipment in many parts of a city and in a much shorter time. Moreover, by varying humidity, wind velocity, and temperature, a variety of weather conditions could, in principle, be simulated so that the final results might be more applicable to different urban environments.

The main advantages of this approach over other methods discussed in this study are that most of the intervening variables, which otherwise could becloud our results, can easily be held constant and much more accurate measurements on all variables are possible. Reliance does not have to placed on the faulty perceptions and memories of interviewees; and if properly designed, such experiments can rule out faulty and inappropriate measurements of air pollution as a reason for the findings obtained. Furthermore, for a given degree of accuracy, this method is likely to be much cheaper than any other. Its main disadvantage is that it tends to overstate the cost of pollution damage. In effect, in most cases, it suggests how people would behave if,rather than try to spread their

---

the case of interior painted surfaces, since an adequate model of such surfaces, which would have to include information on the heating system and the degree to which the building is sealed from outside influences, is likely to be very expensive. For this case it might be possible to classify existing buildings according to heating system and degree of sealing, take a sample in each category, obtain the cooperation of the owners (perhaps even by providing paint) to determine pollution levels specific to the location, and carry out periodic inspections of the painted surfaces.

losses, they attempted to offset completely (at a given level of tastes) the direct damage that would otherwise be inflicted by the pollution. In most cases, especially where other methods fail, this may be a small price to pay. If reasonably accurate measurements of soiling and materials-damage costs due to air pollution are desired, this method of approach should be given a serious hearing.

5

Chapter 4 employed survey methods to study individual adjustments to various commonly experienced levels of pollution. This chapter uses similar methods to measure the costs incurred when pollution levels in a community are far above normal. It is an application of the second measurement strategy described in Chapter 2. While special episodes do not normally justify generalization to other situations, this particular case is less unique than most, and illustrates an approach that could be used in other situations.

The incident occurred on the evening of Friday, March 26, 1965, when clouds of soot were emitted from the Syracuse University steam plant for about twenty minutes. Some residents within a small, well-defined area of Syracuse awoke the next morning to find substantial cleaning tasks facing them. About a week after the episode, researchers went into the area to gather information on the economic costs involved.

THE EPISODE AND ITS EFFECTS ON POLLUTION LEVELS

At about 10:45 p. m. , one of three coal burners at the steam plant stopped firing. An unusually large amount of partially burned and unburned pulverized coal was introduced from this burner into the smokestack dust precipitators, and the amount of coal going to the two remaining burners was increased. As a result, about 300 pounds of waste particles -- finely granulated coal and fly ash -- were ejected into the atmosphere over a period of twenty minutes. The normal emission rate is about 75 pounds in twenty minutes.

The next morning, the ground downwind from the stack
was covered with a sooty, oily substance capable of floating
on water. The sooty, oily character of the pollutant perhaps
intensified the consequent soiling beyond what would have
been expected from the seemingly small amount of pollution
emitted. [1]

The weather condition was another factor that made the
soiling characteristics of this event unusually severe. When
the malfunction occurred, the wind was blowing at an abnormally high speed -- 17 knots -- directly from the West. At
10:00 p. m. the cloud ceiling was 800 feet; by 11:00 p. m. it
had risen to 1200 feet. Much turbulence and mixing were
evident at low elevations. The combination of these conditions
would tend to concentrate the fall-out of stack particles in a
smaller sector than would be affected under less adverse
conditions.

The elevation of the steam plant is roughly 175 feet below
most of the area on which the soot and fall-out occurred at the
same time, the steam station smokestack is 175 feet high, so
that the plane of intersection of the stack top with the affected
area is approximately horizontal. Moreover, as indicated by
the contour lines of Figure 3, the topography of the affected
area is quite irregular.

In the absence of direct measurements of air pollution in
the affected area, relative pollution levels at various downwind locations were estimated with the Pasquill diffusion
equation:[2]

---

[1]It has been estimated that a single gram of pulverized or
partially burned coal is easily capable of blackening ten bed-
sheets. Correspondence dated May 26, 1965, from Gerard A.
DeMarrais, Robert A. Taft Sanitary Engineering Center, Cincinnati, Ohio.

[2]"Atmospheric Diffusion Computations, " Meteorological
Aspects of Air Pollution, Course Manual, Robert A. Taft
Sanitary Engineering Center, Cincinnati, Ohio.

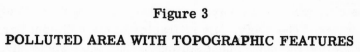

Figure 3

POLLUTED AREA WITH TOPOGRAPHIC FEATURES

Map Source: U.S. Department of the Interior, Geological
          Survey, Washington, D.C.   Revised 1956 <u>Syracuse</u>
          <u>West Quadrangle</u> & <u>Syracuse East Quadrangle</u>.

93

$$D = \frac{1}{u6_Y6_Z} \ \exp \ \frac{-H^2}{26_Z^2} \ \exp \ \frac{-Y^2}{26_Y^2}$$

where D = dilution factor
     u = wind speed
    6_Y = standard deviations of horizontal plume-concentra-
        tion-distribution
    6_Z = standard deviations of vertical plume-concentration-
        distribution
    H = height of emission source above ground level
    Y = horizontal displacement from plume centerline.

This equation assumes a Gaussian distribution of the plume in both horizontal and vertical dimensions, a distribution often exhibited by smoke plumes.

This equation applies to downwind points on the ground at the same elevation as the stack base. In spite of the fact that the affected area is 175 feet higher than the stack base, it is reasonable to assume that the smoke plume formed by emission maintained its centerline distance from the ground as it moved downwind (eastward). That is, the high wind velocity pushed the volume of air at the emission point along with the plume, helping the plume to maintain its height above the ground even though the land rises to the east. This assumption is supported by two additional considerations. First, approximately 60 per cent of the material emitted was estimated to have been smaller than 20 microns and therefore to be suspended particulates. Second, larger particles, which have a slight fall velocity, probably behaved much like the suspended particulates due to the high wind speed.[3]

The pollution zones appearing in Figure 4 were computed using the foregoing equation. The due-east line represents the trace of the smoke plume centerline. These pollution zone values give the best available estimate of the relative magnitude

---

[3]Correspondence with Gerard A. Demarrais, op.cit.

of soot and ash fall-out resulting from the Syracuse University steam plant malfunction. [4]

THE SURVEY DESIGN

The development of the survey instrument and the selection of the sample were strongly influenced by the desire to collect data within a short time after the incident occurred. It was believed that more accurate answers, as well as more cooperation, would be obtained while the pollution was still visible and memories and attitudes still fresh. This consideration ruled out the development of a well-structured questionnaire which, in any case, would have been difficult to construct because of the diversity of experiences and sources from which data had to come.

As an alternative, in interviewing householders, an interview schedule which combined a check list with suggested ways of asking the questions, plus some structured questions where they could be worked out in time, were drawn up. (See Appendix E.) Considerable time was spent instructing the interviewers, who then conducted their own brief pretests and helped in the final revision of the questionnaire. Since substantial latitude was permitted for them to form their own questions, there were some differences in the quality of schedules collected by different persons, but these did not appear to be serious. In interviewing maintenance personnel in the University and local hospitals and commercial establishments, open-ended interviews -- all of which were conducted by the same person-- were obtained.

---

[4]A better pollution indicator probably would have been data obtained from dustfall measurement devices in the affected area. Unfortunately, Syracuse has no air-pollution sampling network.

Figure 4

POLLUTION ZONES AND INTERVIEW LOCATIONS

Syracuse U.
Steam Station

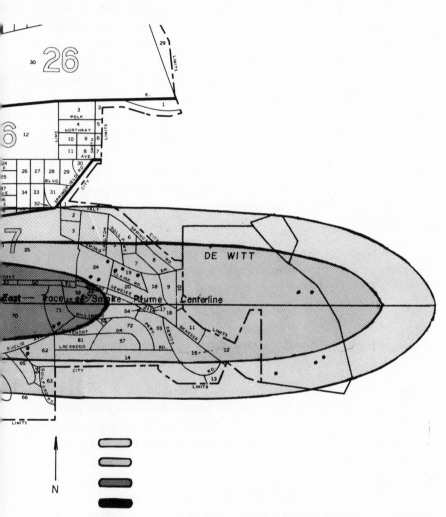

N

Map Source: U.S. Censuses of Population and Housing: 1960
City Blocks Syracuse, N.Y., U.S. Government
Printing Office, Washington 25, D.C.

The questionnaire was designed with four purposes in mind. The first was to collect data relevant for calculating the costs of the incident: hours spent in cleaning tasks, estimated hourly wage for various chores as given by the respondent, cleaning material costs, professional rug cleanings, and the like. This section consisted mainly of a check list designed to remind the interviewer of the types of cost data that should be collected when appropriate. The second purpose was to collect background data such as age and estimated value of property for control purposes. The third was to attempt to measure psychic costs by asking "willingness-to-pay" questions. Finally, two questions were included to determine whether the incident had any effect upon attitudes toward public expenditures.

The time constraint also influenced the sample design. Visual inspection of the area east of Syracuse University soon after the soot and fall-out occurred provided the first estimates of the extent of the affected area. Fortunately, this initial designation proved to be fairly accurate, if confidence can be placed in the pollution values computed using the Pasquill diffusion equation.

An attempt was made to collect the data so that representative samples were gathered at points with varying pollution levels. This was done by contrasting the residential location of persons interviewed with the affected area, likely pollution levels, and interviews taken to date on a day-to-day basis. Table 9 gives some indication of the sample concentration within designated pollution bands. Examination of Figure 4 (each dot represents a sample interview in the affected area) indicates the geographic dispersion of the sample.

ANALYSIS OF DATA

The data are analyzed in two stages: a first approximation of institutional and household costs without control data, and an improved estimate of household costs corrected for the influences of a number of intervening variables.

Table 9

INTERVIEWS UNDERTAKEN BY POLLUTION ZONES

Area by Pollution Index	Housing Units[a]	No. of Interviews Taken	Interviews as % of Housing Units
0-100	1177	51	4.3
101-300	1372	32	2.3
301-600	668	19	2.8
601-900	367	20	5.5
Total	3584	122	3.4

[a]The numbers of housing units involved were computed using the pollution contours drawn in Figure 4 and housing data as given in U.S. Censuses of Population and Housing: 1960 City Blocks, Syracuse, N. Y. (Washington, D. C.: U. S. Government Printing Office, 1962), except for housing units outside the Syracuse city limits which were counted by personal inspection of the area.

First Approximation

Cleaning cost data were collected from four major institutions in the affected pollution area. Discussions with supervisory maintenance personnel at two of these institutions (Syracuse University and the Syracuse VA Hospital) disclosed that cost figures for them are underestimates because of maintenance budget constraints. For example, nurses on duty at the time of the incident were required to make many additional linen changes beyond their normal duties. No additional personnel were called in to help perform these extra duties. In the absence of a budget constraint, it is likely that additional personnel would have been employed or more overtime allowed to perform the extra tasks required by the pollution incident. The present cost estimates do not include a factor for such "extra effort."

Most of the cleaning performed by householders was undertaken during the weekend immediately following the incident
and therefore, for most people, involved a sacrifice of their
leisure time. To place a monetary value on an hour of such
leisure time, two approaches can be used. One involves the
use of the least costly monetary alternative open to the individual. For most, this is likely to be the wage at which they
could have hired someone to do the work for them. [5] If such
a person were available but not hired, the value of an hour of
leisure time given up must be either equal to or less than
this wage rate. The second approach is to ask the individual
how much he would have been willing to pay to have someone
else perform the work for him. If an hour of leisure foregone is considered less costly by the individual than the market alternative, the response to this question should be closer
to the correct value. Furthermore, if no one else is available
to hire, this approach is the only correct one (assuming, of
course, the answer in fact represents what the individual
would have paid). Since both possibilities are present, this
second approach was used except where someone was in fact
hired to perform the cleaning chores.

In fact, however, the responses to the question, "What
would you be willing to pay someone else to perform these
extra cleaning tasks?," indicate that in this case both approaches give roughly the same results. The mean wage given
in response to this question was $1.37 per hour, which is close
to the minimum wage they would have had to pay (and the variance around this wage was small). Furthermore, some respondents seemed to interpret the question as meaning, "What
would you have to pay someone else to perform these extra

---

[5]The use of the individual's wage is sometimes advocated.
However, it would only be correct to consider this price if the
alternative of giving up leisure to receive more income is in
fact possible, an unlikely alternative in this case.

tasks?" To the extent that the responses reflect this interpretation, the method used does not differ in practice from
the first approach and is therefore likely to overestimate the
true cost of the leisure time foregone.

Table 10 presents cost estimates using data gathered from
institutions and householders. Household maintenance costs
are grouped by pollution zone and multiplied by total housing
units in each zone to obtain an estimate of the costs to the
total population in the affected area. It is likely but not certain that this total figure underestimates the true costs.
While the value of leisure time is likely to be an overestimate, costs to institutions were underestimated and, as
explained below, insufficient evidence was obtained on psychic
costs to add in this category.

Improved Cost Estimates

Differences in responses to questions concerning the cost
of clean up after the malfunction could be explained by many
variables other than the pollution itself. To obtain a cost
curve which is independent of the effect of these intervening
variables, as well as to refine the total cost estimate, responses to questions pertaining to such variables have been
combined with the pollution index in a multiple-regression
model.

The dependent variable for this analysis is the cost of
household cleaning and repair (time costs valued at the wage
rate given by the respondent) plus the cost of automobile
cleaning.[6] Settled insurance claims were not included because
virtually no information was available for the independent variables associated with these claims. Furthermore, the different

---

[6]Equations were also tried with house and auto costs sepa-
rated and with leisure time valued at a standard minimum
wage. These variations did not improve the fit and sometimes
made it worse.

Table 10

CLEANING AND DAMAGE COSTS OF SYRACUSE
POLLUTION INCIDENT

Pollution Index	Average Residential Cost[a]	Residential Units Involved[b]	Total Cost
0-100	$ 6.08	1,177	$ 7,156.00
101-300	7.88	1,372	10,811.00
301-600	9.20	668	6,146.00
601-900	11.64	367	4,272.00
Total Residential Cleaning[c]			$28,385.00
Insurance Claims[d] (Residences Only)			6,784.55
V.A. Hospital[e]			553.00
Crouse-Irving Hospital[e]			668.00
Upstate Medical Center[e]			1,012.59
Syracuse University[e]			1,059.53
Grand Total			$38,462.67

[a] Average cost includes labor and material costs, automobile-washing charges and "other" costs (professional rug cleaning, etc.). The average figure for each pollution zone was computed using cost estimates gathered from persons interviewed in the areas indicated by the pollution contours drawn in Figure 2.

[b] The number of residential units involved was computed using the pollution contours drawn in Figure 2 and housing data as given in: U.S. Censuses of Population and Housing: 1960 City Blocks, Syracuse, N.Y. (U.S. Government Printing Office, Washington, D.C., 1962.) Except for housing units outside the Syracuse city limits which were counted by personal inspection of the area.

[c] Application of the average "cleaning costs" figure for all inter-viewed residential occupants to total housing units involved (without regard to pollution index variation) gives a slightly higher total residential cost: $28,457.

[d] The figure for insurance claims reflects settled claims reduced by cleaning costs for those cases where a residence was included in both interview data and insurance claim data. The overlapping was not very extensive; total reduction in insurance claims amounted to $23.08. Six claims were still outstanding at the time of compilation of this table.

[e] Includes both labor and material costs.

scales required to plot household and automobile costs
(Figure 5) and insurance claims (Figure 6) make it clear that
these two sets of data represent different populations and are
likely to be influenced by quite different variables. The independent variables that were tried in addition to pollution are
house location (mid-street = 1, corner = 0);
portion of house facing steam plant (front or side = 1,
back = 0);
number of household members;
respondent classification (head = 1, wife or child = 0);
property value; and
householder's status (owner = 1, renter = 0).
Unfortunately, indications of householder's income and standards of cleanliness were not obtained. The omission of income
is not serious, since property value is likely to be an adequate
proxy. However, as we shall see, cleanliness standards are
probably an important omission.

The most important a priori consideration about the proper
form for the equation to be fitted is that it should show the respondent's cost of clean up to be zero if the pollution index appropriate for him is zero. This consideration means that one
observation (zero cost where pollution is zero) differs from all
others in that it does not include a random error; it is an
absolutely correct observation and therefore the regression
line should be constrained to pass through this point.[7] Where
more than one independent variable is used, an appropriate
equation form to reflect this condition is

$$Y = aX_1^b X_2^c \ldots X_n^h \qquad (1)$$

which in logarithmic form can be fitted by standard least-

_____

[7]At considerably greater and unnecessary cost we could
have assured that the regression equation reflected this fact
by taking a sufficient number of observations on households
outside the affected area.

Figure 5

SCATTER DIAGRAM OF CLEANING COSTS AGAINST AIR-POLLUTION INDEX[a]

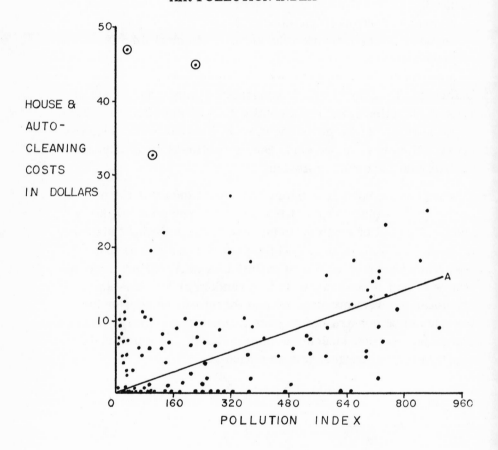

[a]The pollution index is likely to be inaccurate for the circled observations. They represent houses at locations considerably elevated above the surrounding area and appear to have been damaged more severely than nearby houses at lower elevations.

Figure 6

SCATTER DIAGRAM OF INSURANCE CLAIMS AGAINST AIR-
POLLUTION INDEX[a]

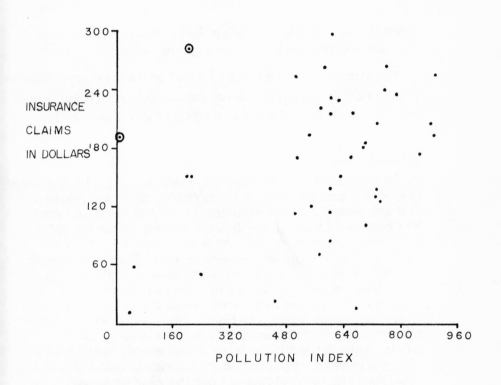

[a]See footnote to Figure 5.

squares methods. [8] A second possibility is to fit a standard
linear regression equation but to assume that costs fall to zero
below a certain pollution threshold. In this case,

$$Y = a + bX_1 + cX_2 + \ldots hX_n \text{ for } X_1 \geq t; \tag{2}$$
$$Y = 0 \text{ for } X_1 < t,$$

where X_1 is the pollution index and t is the threshold value to
be chosen. If only one independent variable is used, an appropriate equation form is

$$Y = bX_1 \tag{3}$$

which is equivalent to the simple least-squares regression
equation constrained to pass through the origin.

The attempt to fit Equations 1 and 2 proved to be unsatisfacto
In both cases, the percentage of explained variance was low, [9]
and the coefficient attached to property value was negative

---

[8] A problem arises in doing so, however, since the equation
cannot be fitted properly if any variables have observations
that are zero (since the logarithm of zero is negative infinity).
The dummy variables, the dependent variable and the pollution
index take on values of zero for some observations. The
dummy variables can be rescaled by replacing the zero with
one and the one with any appropriate number, for example,
two. (Just as zero multiplied by a constant has no effect on a
sum, so a one raised to a power has no effect on a product.)
Observations for which pollution is zero can be left out, since
the dependent variable must also be zero in these cases.
So far as the dependent variable is concerned, rescaling by
adding a constant requires that it be added to both sides of the
equation, with the consequence that the right-hand side is no
longer a simple product. The alternative of leaving out those
observations for which the dependent variable is zero was
taken here, although this solution is not completely satisfactory.

[9] The coefficient of determination for Equation 1 is 0.21 and
for Equation 2 is 0.04.

(indicating that more expensive homes had lower costs of clean up). For Equation 1 only pollution, age of respondent, and property value had coefficients significantly different from zero; and in Equation 2 only the dichotomous variable indicating position of the house was significant. Furthermore, as can be observed in Figure 5, there is no obvious threshold value for pollution below which costs drop off sharply. Variations of Equation 2, some involving second-degree terms and some leaving out observations with zero values for pollution, clean up costs or both, do not improve matters.

There may be several explanations for these results. First, the Pasquill diffusion equation may be in error in predicting that the pollution was carried as far east as indicated in Figure 4. This is possible since the equation assumes that all the pollution was neutrally buoyant and that the land is perfectly flat, neither of which is perfectly correct in our case. This possibility, coupled with the fact that property values tend to rise as one moves east of the pollution source, [10] could explain the negative value for the coefficient attached to property values. If property values correlate negatively and strongly enough with the true pattern of fall-out and if there is no adequate pollution index, then property value could be serving as a (negative) proxy for the true pollution levels.

The second explanation for this result may be that there was no control for cleanliness standards. It is widely observed that upper middle-class housewives have somewhat lower cleanliness standards than those in the lower middle class. Since property values are correlated with such class distinctions, they are also likely therefore to be negatively correlated with cleanliness standards. Furthermore, since the affected neighborhood includes only middle-class families, it is quite

---

[10]Actually, property values fall somewhat for the last 7-8,000 feet, but the sample size is so small for this area that the general effect is a rise.

possible for this correlation to dominate other effects that
property values might have on the costs of cleaning. In this
case, as the property values rise, the cost of clean up would
fall for houses in the same pollution zone.

The inability to control for cleanliness standards can also
explain the absence of an observable threshold. If all persons
in the sample held the same standard of cleanliness and if this
standard involved a threshold, a cross-section view of Equation 2
after being fitted to such data would appear something like
curve OS_2S_2 in Figure 7. But since our sample involves individuals with different standards, some of which may involve
thresholds that occur at or close to zero, a scatter diagram of
all observations is unlikely to portray this neat configuration.
If we were to plot scatters of points around each of the three
curves representing different standards in Figure 7, this point
would be illustrated.

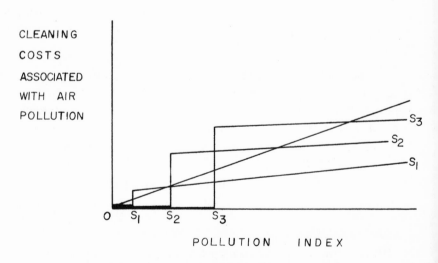

Figure 7: **HYPOTHETICAL RELATIONSHIP BETWEEN CLEANIN
COSTS AND AIR POLLUTION.**

Given that there are no controls for standards and that none of the independent variables enters importantly into a reasonable equation, Equation 3 with the pollution index as the independent variable seems to best represent the situation. It satisfies the requirement that zero costs be associated with zero pollution levels and corresponds reasonably well to the expectations suggested in Figure 7. If individual observations are really clustered around (unobserved) curves such as OS_1S_1, OS_2S_2, and OS_3S_3, a scatter of observations would be dense around the abscissa near the origin, above the regression line $Y = bX_1$ for low values of X_1 (the pollution index) and below that line for high values of X_1. This is roughly the picture actually observed in Figure 5 where the line OA depicts the regression equation, Equation 3. The value for the regression coefficient in that equation is 0.0178 with a standard error of 0.0022 (indicating that the regression coefficient is highly significant.)[11, 12]

This equation, then, is our best estimate of the cost-of-pollution curve for this episode and can be used to indicate the way costs increase with pollution levels. It can also be used to obtain an alternative total cost estimate by calculating the cost to individual households for different levels of pollution and multiplying by the number of households faced with each level of pollution.

The result, presented in Table 11, is a substantially lower figure than that presented in Table 10. While the same general biases are involved in both methods, [13] this difference can be

---

[11]The correlation coefficient was 0.59 but is incorrect because the computer program calculated this coefficient based upon the assumption that the line passes through the means of the variables when, in fact, it does not.

[12]Figure 5 presents a scatter diagram for settled insurance claims. These data were not included in Equation 3 because, as pointed out above, they appear to represent a different population.

[13]Both methods leave out psychic costs and overestimate the value of leisure time for households.

explained by the differential treatment of the few very high-cost observations in the lowest pollution zone; the weighted average method used in Table 10 gives them undue weight and the regression method virtually ignores them.[14] Had the regression method been able to explain any additional variance by incorporating one or more of the intervening variables, it would have provided a superior estimate of the total cost of the incident. As it is, these two estimates are best used to provide upper and lower bounds within which the true figure is likely to fall.

PSYCHIC COSTS AND ATTITUDES TOWARD EXPENDITURES ON AIR-POLLUTION CONTROL

In this study, psychic costs are understood to refer to losses beyond the resource costs that this incident might have caused.[15] The only way to obtain an estimate of psychic costs is to ask people how much they would have been willing to pay to have avoided the incident altogether and to subtract from this figure, which logically should be at least as much as the direct expenses involved, the actual costs incurred.

---

[14]These extreme observations raise the mean of the costs for the pollution zone in which they lie and are given heavy weight by the first method, since a large proportion of the houses fell within this low pollution zone. By contrast, by forcing the regression line through the origin, they are given virtually no weight by the second method.

Had there been more time and more accurate pollution measurements available so that a better judgment could have been made as to whether these observations are representative of the total population or not, we might have found good reason to eliminate them from the sample. In this case, the weighted average method would have yielded the best single estimate of the total cost of this incident.

[15]See the discussion of psychic costs in Chapter 2.

Table 11

IMPROVED COST ESTIMATES

Category of "Cost"	Amount
Residential Cleaning Costs Stratified by Pollution Index	
0-100	$ 999.00
101-300	4445.00
301-600	5090.00
601-900	4881.00
Subtotal: Residential Cleaning	$15,415.00
Claims and Institutional Cleaning Costs[a]	10,079.00
Grand Total	$25,494.00

[a]Obtained from Table 10.

Table 12

TABULATION OF RESPONSES
TO WILLINGNESS-TO-PAY QUESTION

Measured Costs	Willingness- to-Pay Costs	Psychic Costs
$ 9.45	$10.00	$ .55
43.75	50.00	6.25
45.61	45.61	.00
19.28	25.00	5.72
15.67	25.00	9.33
25.32	30.00	4.68
13.59	25.00	11.41
12.95	20.00	7.05
4.25	4.25	.00
8.79	8.79	.00

111

Unfortunately, many responses to the willingness-to-pay questions[16] could not be used. Typical of these were:

"I really don't know."

"Nothing. I work hard for my money. I'll sue the city. It's all their fault."

"I don't think you can keep an explosion from happening. I wouldn't pay anything."

"One dollar for insurance to prevent it."

Others gave figures that were below their own estimate of their actual costs.

However, in spite of the apparent difficulty that many had in interpreting the questions correctly, eleven individuals out of a total of 85 who had any costs at all gave usable answers. These are presented in Table 12. These responses are too few to be considered representative of psychic costs generally for the affected population. But they are encouraging because they suggest that at least a small number of respondents can interpret and answer such questions properly.

It is instructive to note the effect of this episode on attitudes toward public expenditures for different services, one of which was air-pollution control. Questions A and B on the fourth page of the questionnaire were included for this purpose. While few were willing to give numerical answers to Question A, most (113 out of 122) were willing to indicate a desire to increase, decrease, or keep constant the level of taxes going to the listed services. Table 13 presents a tabulation of the responses to this question. In response to Question B, 39 respondents indicated a desire for increased expenditure on pollution control out of an increase in taxes, the mean increase

---

[16]For the exact wording of this question, see the third page of the questionnaire in Appendix E.

Table 13

QUESTION A TABULATION

Question[a] Category	Per Cent Giving Indicated Response			
	Increase	Decrease	Same	Didn't Know
Education	65	5	26	4
Fire Protection	6	4	83	7
Police Protection	72	2	25	1
Refuse Collection and Disposal	12	6	79	3
Air-Pollution Control	40	5	38	17
Streets and Highways	39	10	46	5
Public Health and Hospitals	16	42	33	9
Relief and Welfare	9	47	35	9
Cultural and Recreational Facilities	44	11	42	3

[a]See Appendix E.

113

desired being 2.5 per cent with the remainder divided between the other services. As one would expect, those who were most hurt by the incident were most desirous of increasing expenditures: these 39 households spent an average of $10.50 for cleaning due to this incident which is substantially above the average cleaning costs of $7.10 for all 122 respondents.

CHAPTER **6** PROPERTY VALUES
AND AIR POLLUTION:
A CROSS-SECTION
STUDY OF ONE CITY

The third strategy outlined in Chapter 2 for measuring the
costs of air pollution involves the use of residential property
values. Available evidence leaves little doubt that air pollution can affect health, irritate the eyes, nose, and throat,
corrode metal and stone, discolor and dirty buildings outside
and in, and in general blight a neighborhood. There is also
some evidence from questionnaire studies that people believe
air pollution affects property values and that it sometimes influences their decisions to move. [1] While it is reasonable to
assume that many of these detrimental effects are reflected in
property values, there has been almost no reliable statistical
evidence bearing on this hypothesis. The main purpose of the
research reported in this and the next chapter is to provide
such evidence.

---

[1]Public Administration and Metropolitan Affairs Program,
Southern Illinois University, Public Awareness and Concern
with Air Pollution in the St. Louis Metropolitan Area, dittoed,
(Edwardsville, Ill.: Southern Illinois University, 1964); Walter
S. Smith, Jean J. Schueneman and Louis D. Zeidberg, "Public
Reaction to Air Pollution in Nashville, Tennessee," Journal of
Air Pollution Control Association, Vol. 14, No. 10, October,
1964, pp. 418-23; and Peter Rossi, Why Families Move
(Glencoe, Ill.: The Free Press, 1955), p. 82.

This chapter applies least-squares regression methods to a cross-section of observations on single-family dwelling units in an urban area to obtain estimates of the effect of variations in air pollution on the property values of these units.

Since the focus of the study is on estimating the relevant regression coefficients rather than on the simple statistical explanation of variations in the dependent variable, the effects of multicollinearity (large non-zero correlations among the explanatory variables) cannot be ignored by arguing that the explanatory power of the fitted equation as a whole is not affected by its presence. With respect to the air-pollution variable, the method of treating this problem involves the development of several alternative estimates of its effects, each based upon a different assumption concerning the independent contribution of pollution given other explanatory variables. These estimates have the property that they would be identical to the conventional one if air pollution were completely uncorrelated with the remaining explanatory variables.

THE MODEL AND VARIABLES USED

The form and content of this study are determined to a large extent by two considerations. First, the data available consist of a cross-section of observations by census tracts within a single metropolitan area.[2] This leads to the use of explanatory

---

[2]Time-series data are not available; and cross-section data between cities present serious difficulties because of differences in measurement procedures as well as differences in the effects of pollution when meteorological conditions and the pollution "mix" are not held constant (to say nothing of the additional problems that would be involved in explaining property values).

Census tracts are used as the units of observation primarily for convenience. However, quite apart from the fact that most of the data are available by these units, there are some advantages in using averages by census tracts instead of individual

variables that pertain primarily to the physical and neighborhood characteristics of the property. A given residential unit
is assumed to consist of a "bundle" of attributes present in
varying degrees, each of which has an implicit market price
(positive or negative), the market value of this unit being the
sum of the values of these attributes.[3]

Since we can expect to find a good deal of matching of housing and family characteristics (e.g., larger families living in
larger houses), variables of either type could be used to predict property values.[4] However, the market value of a given

---

observations, assuming the sample size to be the same in both
cases. Errors in estimating the value of individual houses
tend to wash out; fewer explanatory variables, particularly
those related to the idiosyncracies of individual houses and
their owners, need be considered; and the air-pollution data
available are more accurate when applied to neighborhoods than
when applied to individual houses within a neighborhood.

Since the census information is based upon owners' apprais-
als, there is, of course, the danger that large response errors
are present. According to one study, however, this is not the
case for averages: the difference between the means of ap-
praisers' and owners' estimates for 568 homes was only $350.
See Leslie Kish and John B. Lansing, "Response Errors in
Estimating the Value of Homes," American Statistical Association Journal, Vol. 49, 1954, pp. 520-32. Furthermore,
errors in difference between average property values in different tracts are likely to be even smaller.

[3] This viewpoint may be contrasted with that of a study the
purpose of which is to explain family housing expenditures with
cross-section data. While the dependent variable may be the
same, in this case the explanatory variables pertain to the
characteristics of the owner-occupants of the property. This
viewpoint may also be contrasted with that of a study utilizing
time-series data for a given house or group of houses; in this
case determinants of market demand, which again mean mainly
occupant characteristics, are the most important variables.

[4] Indeed, we have found that parsimony and convenience ar-

house is determined by the demand (for particular sets of attributes) of all potential buyers, not just the demand of its current occupants; and within a given market (assuming no dis-
crimination) the determinants of this demand (aggregate income
the distribution of income, family size, etc.) are constant in
cross-section data. If, therefore, we are interested in explaining differences in the values of properties available to the same
set of purchasers, it should be done in terms of differences in
the characteristics of the properties rather than in terms of
differences in the characteristics of their owner-occupants. In
the absence of adequate measures of property characteristics
we may wish to use highly correlated occupant characteristics,
but it should be understood that the latter are being used as
proxies for the missing variables, not as direct determinants of
property values. Explicit mention is made of this fact because
in at least one case, we use an occupant characteristic (family
income) in this way.

The situation is different, however, if the cross-section observations pertain to more than one market, for then the characteristics of the house as well as the characteristics of the
potential purchasers may differ between census tracts. As a
first approximation in some studies, it may be sufficient to assume that the whole urban area comprises a single unified
housing market. But particularly because the location of some
submarkets in our case study tends to be associated with different levels of air pollution, we prefer to introduce some explicit recognition of the presence of these submarkets.

---

gue in favor of relying on only two variables, median family
income (an occupant characteristic) and median number of
rooms (a property attribute). With our data, it takes a regression equation containing ten different variables pertaining
to property characteristics, some of which were measured
specifically for this study, to approximately equal the explanatory value of an equation with these two variables.

The second consideration that has significantly influenced this study has been our a priori expectation that the impact of air pollution on property value (as judged in terms of the partial correlation coefficients or the standardized beta weights) is likely to be small relative to that of other variables. This belief has led us, in most runs, to restrict the sample of observations to census tracts in which single-family housing units as a percentage of total housing units are at least 60 per cent and the population density is at least one person per acre. These restrictions, which reduce the sample size from a total of 304 to 167,[5] were introduced as the only method available to separate predominantly rural, commercial, and industrial tracts from predominantly urban residential areas. By concentrating on the latter, considerable homogeneity with respect to market influences on single-family housing units is obtained, while little is lost with respect to variations in the air-pollution levels experienced.[6] For comparison, one run using all census tracts has been included in the summary table of final results presented below.[7]

---

[5]Actually, the 1960 census for St. Louis divides the area into 345 tracts, but data for median property values were not available for 17, and reasonable interpolation of air-pollution data could not be made for an additional 24 of these tracts.

[6]In particular, the elimination of predominantly industrial tracts has the advantage of reducing the correlation between air pollution and other social disamenities associated with proximity to industry. It is less likely, therefore, that the pollution variable is picking up the effects of industrial noise, conjestion, and eyesores. Furthermore, the elimination of tracts with a predominance of multifamily dwelling units makes variables such as median number of rooms per unit, which unfortunately is available only for all dwelling units, more representative of the true figures for single-family units than they otherwise would be.

[7]A comparison of runs containing the same variables for the total and the restricted sample tend to bear out these conten-

This belief has also led to the inclusion of a wider variety and number of variables than is generally included in property value studies. A useful rule of thumb is to include all variables that are likely to be at least as important as the variable of primary interest; for then it is reasonably likely that the primary variable will not prove to be significant only because it happened to be correlated with some more important variable that was left out of the analysis.

On the basis of these considerations data on the variables described below were gathered and tried in various runs. The variables have been roughly grouped into categories according to our judgment of their role in explaining property values, and hypotheses concerning the likely form of their relationship with the dependent variable are presented. A detailed description with sources and methods of measurement can be found in Appendix F.

Air Pollution

To date there is no commonly accepted index for the general phenomenon called air pollution. In consultation with air-pollution experts familiar with the St. Louis data, two measures of pollution were chosen for trial in this study. In both cases the annual geometric mean was used as the measure of central tendency. The first, a measure of sulfation levels which for convenience is given the symbol SUL, is an index indicating the presence of SO_2, SO_3, H_2S, H_2SO_4, and in some instances dustfall.[8] The compound SO_2 can damage freshly applied paint,

---

tions. For the total sample, the multiple R^2 as well as the F values for many regression coefficients were considerably lower, in spite of the larger sample size. While some coefficients were substantially different, curiously, that for SUL, the air-pollution variable, was quite similar to those found for the restricted sample. Compare Equation 5 with others, especially 1 and 2 given in Table 14.

[8]Coal burning is the principle source of both dustfall and

making it dry more slowly, making it more permeable to water and, over its lifetime causing it to flake off more rapidly. The compound H_2S can also damage and discolor paints and, along with H_2SO_4, corrode metal and stone. They can also irritate the eyes, nose and throat, and cause damage to vegetation. The second measure of pollution tried is a measure of suspended particulates gathered by high-volume air samplers. In the absence of a sufficient number of sampling stations to permit use of dustfall measurements, this measure of suspended particulates was used as an indicator of soiling. However, it is not by itself well suited for this purpose, since the particles it measures are sufficiently small that they are as likely to be blown off surfaces as to stick and cause damage.

After a number of trials using both indexes, the suspended-particulates measure was finally dropped. Statistically, it gave unsatisfactory results; the partial regression coefficients between it and property value were generally positive. Moreover, it was not measured as accurately as sulfation; samples were collected from only 16 stations as compared to 41 for sulfation. [9] Finally, since a reasonably high correlation was found between the few measurements of dustfall available and sulfation, the suspended particulate measure proved not to be essential as an index of soiling.

While air pollution is generally assumed to be negatively related to property values (other things being equal) there are no commonly accepted hypotheses about any more specific form that this relationship might take.

---

sulfation in the St. Louis area; the simple correlation coefficient between the two is .54.

[9]Measurements at specific stations are equally accurate, but they were used to obtain isopleth maps from which values for each census tract were obtained. Interpolation by this method from only 16 census tracts can result in very inaccurate estimates.

Characteristics Specific to the Property

As indicators of characteristics of the property itself, median number of rooms (MNR), percentage recently built (PRB), and houses per mile (HPM) were used. MRN is assumed to be a proxy for house size and HPM for lot size. [10] Originally percentage substandard (PSS) was included, but the restrictions on the sample eliminated most of the tracts with high values for this variable and it was dropped from final runs. PRB, which is included as a general index of quality, probably picks up a good part of the influence of factors affecting PSS in any case. MNR and PRB should be positively related and HPM should be negatively related to median property values (MPV).

Location Characteristics

Four variables reflecting different aspects of locational advantages and disadvantages of the property were tried in early runs. The first is based upon a division of the metro-politan area into time zones (TIZ) depending upon express bus travel time during rush hour to the central business district. The other three are dummy variables reflecting accessibility to highways and major thoroughfares (HWA), shopping area accessibility (SAA), and industrial area accessibility (IAA). Assuming that the central business district sufficiently dominates other transportation focal points, or that the dummy variables appropriately control for proximity to these points, TIZ should be negatively related to MPV throughout its whole range. The coefficients for the dummy variables should be positive.

---

[10]HPM serves as a proxy for lot size only in the restricted sample where rural, commercial and industrial tracts, with small values for HPM that do not necessarily reflect lot size, have been left out.

Neighborhood Characteristics

Of the many neighborhood characteristics that may affect property values in addition to air pollution, we have been able to obtain data on school quality (SCH), crime rates (CRR), persons per unit (PPU), and occupation ratio (OCR). School quality is measured using dummy variables indicating residents' attitudes about quality. While data were collected on three categories for SCH, a dichotomous variable with above average in one category and average and below average in the other should be sufficient since it is unlikely that finer distinctions are made by most people. [11]

Ideally we should like to have information on attitudes about school quality and crime rates, although objective measurements may have to be used as proxies in the absence of information about them. It should be clear without elaboration that subjective evaluations more directly determine property values; in addition, the influence of more objective measures is likely to be offset by associated financial changes, especially where residential property owners rather than businesses pay the bulk of the taxes. The effect on property values of increases in teacher salaries or teacher-student ratios -- even if they do reflect actual quality -- is likely to be offset by higher taxes (or lower quality of other services in order to finance better schools); and lower crime rates, which mean lower insurance rates, may also mean higher local taxes to support a more effective police force. While it proved possible to arrive at a simple consensus among knowledgeable persons about general attitudes toward school quality in different parts of the metropolitan area, it was unfortunately not possible to do so with crime rates.

---

[11]This assumption corresponds with the real estate salesman's behavior of pointing out the good qualities, ignoring the mediocre and denying the existence of bad neighborhood characteristics, in talking to potential buyers.

Since we are controlling for houses per square mile, <u>persons per housing unit</u> (PPU) measures population density in residential areas. It is likely to be a better measure of this attribute than population per square mile, because the measure of area includes some nonresidential areas (despite our attempts to control for this by restrictions on the sample). Higher values of PPU are likely to be associated with larger numbers of children in the neighborhood, and consequently more wear and tear on property, more noise, nuisance (where others' children are concerned), possible higher school taxes, and so on. However, this variable could also be considered another indication of the quality of the house itself, at least insofar as more persons per house generally means more depreciation on houses of the same age. [12]

<u>Occupation ratio</u> (OCR) is one of the components of the Shevsky-Bell social area index. [13] It indicated the ratio of craftsmen, foremen, operatives and laborers to total number of employed persons. It is included as a measure of the homogeneity of a neighborhood on the assumption that, in general, people prefer to live in neighborhoods that are homogeneous with respect to broad occupational and social classes. Since high and low values for this variable would reflect such homogeneity, we expect to find property values higher for extreme than for intermediate values.

---

[12] In a study of family housing expenditures this variable would be interpreted as an occupant characteristic reflecting family size, but it is not legitimate to do so here for reasons given earlier.

[13] E. Shevsky and W. Bell, <u>Social Area Analysis</u> (Stanford: Stanford University Press, 1955).

Taxes and Public Services

Taxes and the level and quality of public services provided by them are also likely to be capitalized in the value of the property. Although an adequate introduction of these characteristics would require a special study beyond the scope of this one, the most important differences between census tracts in these regards can easily be incorporated by including a dummy variable (ILL) to indicate whether a census tract is in Illinois (one) or in Missouri (zero). This variable will certainly pick up the effect of differences in property taxes between the two states. Since these taxes are higher in Illinois than in Missouri, other things remaining equal, property values should be higher west of the Mississippi. However, this variable may also pick up the effects of other unknown differences between census tracts in the two states that are not accounted for by the other variables used in this study. Unfortunately, it also may pick up the effect of SUL and for this reason, as explained in the next section, is given special statistical treatment.

Submarket Variables

Of the various submarkets into which the housing market of the St. Louis area can be divided, the most important for our purposes is the nonwhite housing market.   Since the dividing line between the white and nonwhite submarkets is not sharp, a dummy variable cannot be used to make this distinction. [14] Instead a continuous variable representing <u>percentage nonwhite</u> residents in a census tract (PNW) is used.

––––––––––––

[14]It is not sharp in our data since we are using census tracts as units of observation, the boundaries of which seldom coincide with the boundaries of these two markets. But it is also our impression that in the St. Louis area the dividing line between such markets is in fact sometimes fuzzy.

Previous studies have suggested that this variable has a
significant impact on property values, but that the nature of
the relationship varies from city to city and sometimes within
cities, depending upon demand and supply of houses for nonwhites as compared with that for whites, the duration of time
that a particular value of PNW has prevailed, and what is happening in adjacent neighborhoods. [15] Without additional information on each of these factors no a priori judgments about the
form of its relationship with property values can be made.

A question can be raised as to why occupation ratio and percentage nonwhite are given separate treatments and different
interpretations. Should not the former be treated as a sub-
market variable or the latter as a neighborhood characteristic?
The distinction is justified because of the possibility of dis-
crimination against nonwhites. It is this possibility which
generally takes the form of a prohibition against nonwhites
entering certain neighborhoods except at exorbitant prices,
rather than merely a preference for living near members of
one's own class or race, that makes it possible for demand
and supply conditions to differ in different parts of the city.

This point can be emphasized by considering two groups,
A and B, living side by side within a given urban boundary,
both of whom prefer to live with their own kind. If population
in group A expands, additional housing for its members must
be obtained by bidding houses away from members of group B,
thereby raising the average price level. Other things constant,
if the perimeter of group A can expand in this way at will,
there is no reason why the price of houses in A and B should
differ. It is only when the perimeter of group A cannot expand

---

[15]See Luigi Laurenti, Property Values and Race (Berkeley:
University of California Press, 1960), pp. 47-65, and Chester
Rapkin and William G. Grigsby, The Demand for Housing in
Racially Mixed Areas (Berkeley: University of California
Press, 1960), pp. 88-105.

-- or can only do so at discriminatory prices -- that the average price in A will increase relative to that in B.

Median Family Income

The last variable, median family income (MFI) must be given special treatment, for it does not fit into any one of the groups of variables specified above. As indicated, within one market, owner-occupant characteristics have no place in our model, except as proxies for property characteristics that could not be measured. The fact that income is highly correlated with some of the variables that have been included, leads us to believe it is also likely to be so correlated with many of the housing and neighborhood characteristics we have been unable to measure. However, this fact also leads us to prefer a residualized version of this variable (RMF) that has been made orthogonal to the highly correlated variables included in our analysis. The procedure for obtaining this new variable is described below. It should be interpreted as a proxy for the housing and neighborhood characteristics that have not been included in this study.

ADJUSTMENTS FOR MULTICOLLINEARITY

Because our principal goal is to estimate specific regression coefficients (and their associated standard errors), it is necessary to assess and, if needed, to adjust for, the effects of intercorrelation among the independent variables. In general, if the model has been properly specified, least-squares estimates will be unbiased regardless of the extent of multicollinearity. But if a variable that a priori judgment suggests should be included in the analysis is omitted, the regression coefficients for the remaining variables with which it is correlated will be biased. This fact is well known. But it is not so commonly recognized that biased estimates will also be obtained if a variable that a priori judgment suggested should be excluded is for some reason incorrectly included in the regression analysis. The extent of such biases due to incorrect specifica-

tion of the model depends upon the degree of correlation between the variable incorrectly excluded or included and the
variables whose coefficients are critical to the analysis.

There are no cut and dried methods for detecting and treating the problem of multicollinearity. [16] Our procedures involved stepwise regressions to observe the effect on regression
coefficients when new variables are included and, following a
suggestion of Ferrar and Glauber, correlations of each independent variable against all others to observe the magnitudes
of their multiple and partial correlation coefficients. From
these observations, plus a consideration of the effects that
changes in model specification could have on coefficients of
principal interest, a number of areas were selected for special
treatment. Such treatment must involve the introduction of
additional information, whether it be empirical or a priori.
In the absence of an additional sample of data in which such
multicollinearity is negligible, the approach adopted here is to
present alternative estimates of the coefficients of primary interest, each of which is based on a different assumption concerning the extent to which several possible explanatory variables should be included in the regression analysis. In doing so,
we exploit two properties of least-squares estimation methods:
first, that calculated residuals from a least-squares regression equation are orthogonal to the explanatory variables of
that equation, and second, that the inclusion of a regressor
that is orthogonal to previously included regressors will not
bias their estimated coefficients. [17]

------

[16]See J. Johnston, Econometric Methods (New York:
McGraw-Hill, 1963), p. 207; A. S. Goldberger, Econometric
Theory (New York: John Wiley & Sons, Inc., 1964), pp. 192-93;
and D. E. Farrar & R. R. Glauber, "Multicollinearity in
Regression Analysis: The Problem Revisited," Working Paper
105-64, A. P. Sloan School of Management, M.I.T., 1964.

[17]These and other properties of the methods used in this
section are derived by -- or easily derivable from -- A. S.
Goldberger, op. cit., pp. 194-97.

With respect to air pollution, a first estimate of its effect on property values is provided by Equation 1. (See Table 14, p. 134.) This estimate is a conventional one in the sense that no adjustments have been made for multicollinearity.

The second estimate results from a special treatment of the variable ILL. This dummy variable really reflects a number of differences between census tracts in Illinois and Missouri, all of which should be included in our model, but at least one of which is already explicitly included. Since prevailing winds are from the west and northwest and since most of the industry responsible for pollution is located along the Mississippi River, it is reasonable to assume that one such variable already included in the regression model is the sulfation index. The partial correlation coefficient between ILL and sulfation tends to support this contention: its value is 0.35, the second largest observed between ILL and the explanatory variables. [18] To the extent that ILL does measure differences in air pollution, it is improper to include it since sulfation is already present among the regressors. But to leave it out would lead to an improper exclusion of other factors, such as different tax rates, that could explain differences in property values between the two states; this omission could also bias the estimates of the coefficients of other regressors.

A reasonable resolution of this problem is to replace ILL with another variable, RILL, that is orthogonal to sulfation, but not to the other regressors. This new variable is obtained by subtracting from the actual values of ILL the computed values obtained from an auxiliary regression of ILL against sulfation. RILL, in other words, is actual ILL "corrected for"

---

[18]The largest is that between ILL and HWA. Given the definition of HWA (see Appendix F) there is no a priori reason for believing these variables are misspecified. For this reason as well as because HWA is not of major concern to us, no adjustments are made for this particular manifestation of multicollinearity.

sulfation. The observations on RILL are, of course, simply
the residuals from this auxiliary regression, and the adjustment may therefore be referred to as "residualization." The
effect of this adjustment is to attribute to sulfation whatever
covariation exists between it and ILL. The coefficient of sulfation is the same as it would have been had ILL not been included; the coefficients of all other variables, including that
for RILL, are unaffected by this procedure. Equation 2 in
Table 14 presents this estimate of the effect of sulfation on
median property value.

A third estimate of the effect of variations in the level of
sulfation is obtained by regressing residualized median property
value, RMPV, against sulfation. Observations on the variable
RMPV are the residuals from an auxiliary regression of median property value on all the explanatory variables other than
sulfation. The effect of this procedure is to attribute to the
other regressors all the covariation between them and sulfation.
Accordingly, this estimate is the most conservative point estimate of the coefficient of the air pollution variable obtainable
by these methods.

A fourth and final estimate has been obtained by first regressing median property value against all the independent
variables for that subset of tracts for which sulfation is constant at the lowest measured level. The coefficients so obtained were applied to the remaining tracts to obtain an estimate of what median property value would be in each of these
tracts in the absence of air pollution. The difference between
actual median property value and this conditional "prediction"
of median property value was then explained by sulfation in a
regression of these differences on sulfation. [19, 20]

---

[19]This method is analogous to that employed in the construction of a Laspeyre's price index, the numerator of which indicates the present cost of the base period market basket of goods.
Our analogs of the base period quantity weights are the re-

These are the most interesting of the alternative estimates
of the effect of air pollution that were obtained.[21] Among them,

---

gression coefficient for the base air-pollution zone. Just as
current quantities purchased are irrelevant to the interpretation of such a price index, so are the regression coefficients
that actually apply in the moderate-to-high air-pollution zones.
And just as a Laspeyre's index would exactly agree with a
Paasche price index if current and base period quantities were
exactly the same, so would the result yielded by the method
presently under discussion agree exactly with those obtained by
taking the high-pollution zone as the base if regression coefficients for all air-pollution zones were exactly the same. Furthermore, this latter result would be identical to that obtained
by the third method described above. Compare with Z. Griliches,
"Hedonic Price Indexes for Automobiles: An Econometric
Analysis of Quality Change, " U.S. Congress, Joint Economic
Committee, Government Price Statistics, Hearings, January
24, 1961 (Washington: Government Printing Office, 1961).

[20]A variation of this method would involve establishing a
regression equation for MPV (against all variables other than
SUL) for each different air-pollution zone, weighting the coefficients together, and utilizing the weighted coefficients to
obtain RMPV to be regressed against SUL. If weights used for
this purpose are

$$\sum_{r}^{s} x_i^2 / \sum_{1}^{n} x_i^2$$

where the denominator sum is taken over all observations and
the numerator sum is taken over all observations for a given
value of SUL, then it can be shown that the result is identical
to that obtained from the conventional regression used in obtaining RMPV, as in Equation 3.

[21]Still another estimate can be obtained by taking a simple
regression between MPV and SUL. It can be shown that this
represents an application extreme to that used for the second
estimation above. It is equivalent to residualizing each independent variable against SUL, implying that their presence in
the equation will bias the coefficient of SUL unless such an adjustment is made. The value obtained for this coefficient of
SUL is -$1,716. This estimate can be interpreted as the impact

we prefer the second, namely -$245 per unit of sulfation per household. This preference stems from the similarity between the form of the regression equation in which this estimate appears and the a priori model we have in mind. The fact that the first and fourth estimates are not too different from this result leads us to have more confidence in it. The third estimate, which has been deliberately made conservative, can be used as something of a lower bound for a range of reasonable point estimates.

A second area in which model specification is difficult because of multicollinearity pertains to the use of median family income in the regression equations. As in the case of ILL, it is useful to introduce this variable as a proxy for those neighborhood and property characteristics that could not be measured. But median family income is highly correlated with a number of variables explicitly included, with the consequence that estimates of their coefficients are biased by its inclusion. Two different treatments of this variable are presented, one in which income is included in conventional form, and a second in which it is residualized against mean number of rooms, houses per mile and occupation ratio, the variables whose coefficients are most likely to portray such a bias. In this latter form, it serves as a proxy only for those characteristics not explicitly included in the equation. The coefficient of air pollution is not affected by the inclusion of RMFI in place of median family income. [22]

---

on median property values of a unit increase in SUL on the assumption that all observed covariation between SUL and the other explanatory variables reflects the effects of air pollution. Since there are no a priori grounds for believing that this assumption is correct, this estimate is not defensible.

[22]It could be argued that MFI should be residualized against all property and neighborhood characteristics, including SUL, whether the covariance between them is high or not, since the presence of favorable characteristics "causes" families with

The problem of multicollinearity also appeared when quadratic functions were fitted to allow for the possibility of curvilinear or parabolic relationships between median property value and a number of the independent variables. Simple correlations between a variable and its square were generally quite high, at times approaching unity. In order to fit such a function and at the same time avoid the possible misleading implications of large standard errors for the "true" significance of the variable, the <u>form</u> of the parabola was first obtained in the usual way with the variable and its square as separate independent variables. The variable was then transformed to conform to this shape and employed as a single independent variable.[23] This transformation is of the form $(x - a)^2$, where a is the minimum point of the parabola obtained earlier. The statistical significance (or lack thereof) of the variable in question was judged by the standard error of the regression coefficient of this transformed variable.

---

higher incomes to move in, rather than the other way around. Since this treatment is virtually the same as leaving income out altogether, with the consequence that it could not serve as a proxy for anything, we do not favor this approach. It may, however, be of interest to note that the effect of omitting MFI on the regression coefficient of SUL is to lower it to -$259, with a standard error of $109.

[23]This transformation is accomplished by completing the square. Adding $\frac{b^2}{4c} - \frac{b^2}{4c}$ (=0) to the right side of $Y = a + bX + cX^2$ and rearranging terms yields $Y = a - \frac{b^2}{4c} + c(X + \frac{b}{2c})^2$.

It is clear that the coefficient of this transformed variable is simply the coefficient of X^2 in the original quadratic equation, and that the function attains a maximum or minimum value when $X = -\frac{b}{2c}$.

Table 14

ALTERNATIVE ESTIMATION EQUATIONS FOR
MEDIAN PROPERTY VALUES OF 1960 CENSUS TRACTS FOR
THE ST. LOUIS METROPOLITAN AREA
(Standard errors in parentheses)

Variables[a,b]	Eq. 1	Eq. 2	Eq. 3	Eq. 4	Eq. 5
Sample Size	167	167	167	93	304
Dependent Variable	MPV	MPV	RMPV[c]	RSMPV[d]	MPV
Constant	-1469.	-2800.	242.7	734.6	1384
SUL	-186.5 (91.9)	-245.0 (88.1)	-82.97 (59.65)	-248.1 (93.3)	-280.4 (92.9)
MNR	284.1 (46.1)	488.5 (41.1)			349.7 (33.9)
PRB	50.07 (7.02)	48.36 (7.20)			43.85 (7.26)
$(HPM - 2.42)^2$	64.97 (21.57)	116.6 (20.4)			38.39 (6.71)
$(TIZ - 3.82)^2$	337.1 (136.1)	320.2 (138.7)			112.4 (84.4)
HWA	920.0 (273.)	922.5 (278.9)			73.98 (274.6)
SCH1	-1468. (808.)	398.2 (302.2)			-1151. (531.)
SCH2	-1923. (774.)				-1254 (504.)
$(OCR - 0.64)^2$	9847. (2889.)	16940. (2840.)			32660. (2520.)
PPU	-3385. (542.)	-3210. (548.7)			-2013 (430.)
$(PNW + 14)^2$	.1276 (.0655)	.1961 (.0623)			.0271 (.0598)
ILL	-736.3 (361.4)	-819.8 (369.1)			-1786. (368.)
RILL[e]					
MFI	.9330 (.104)	.9374 (.1057)			
RMFI[f]					.8512 (.121)
R^2 (See note g)	.939	.937	.012	.072	.870

134

Notes to Table 14

[a]Variable names and sources are given in Appendix F.

[b]The constants for variables of the form $(x + a)^2$ were obtained from the coefficients of three variables in standard quadratic form utilizing the restricted sample.

[c]$\overline{RMPV} = MPV - \overline{MPV}$ where $\overline{MPV} = 444.3 + 286.4\ MNR + 49.29\ PRB + 66.42\ (HPM - 2.42)^2 + 328.0\ (TIZ - 3.82)^2 + 0.0908\ (PNW + 14)^2 + 1004.\ (SCH - .69)^2 + 11130.\ (OCR - 0.64)^2 + 854.5\ HWA - 1010.\ ILL - 3234.\ PPU + 0.9286\ MFI,\ R^2 = .937.$

[d]$RSMPV = MPV - SMPV$ where $SMPV = 9428. + 398.8\ MNR + 64.60\ PRB - 432.8\ HPM + 103.0\ (HPM)^2 - 4163.3\ TIZ + 484.8\ (TIZ)^2 + 67.45\ PNW - 05957\ (PNW)^2 - 14598.\ OCR + 13534.\ (OCR)^2 + 890.1\ HWA - 3308.\ PPU - 75.32\ ILL + .7611\ MFI,\ R^2 = .930,$ using tracts with the lowest values for SUL.

[e]$RILL = ILL - \overline{ILL}$ where $\overline{ILL} = -0.1507 + 0.1396\ SUL.$

[f]$RMFI = MFI - MFI$ where $MFI = 4396. + 226.7\ MNR + .3064\ (HPM - 2.42)^2 + 6.749\ (OCR - 0.64)^2$

[g]R^2 is the coefficient of multiple determination for Eqs. 1, 2, and 5, and the coefficient of partial determination linking SUL to (residualized) property values for Eqs. 3 and 4.

135

CONCLUSIONS

Table 14 presents the most interesting equations derived
in this study. Equation 2, which incorporates ILL and median
family income in residualized form, is best in our judgment
in that it most closely accords with our a priori beliefs. The
other equations are presented for comparison purposes, the
first being a conventional form of the second, the third providing the most conservative estimate of the effects of air pollution, the fourth representing a different method of adjusting
for multicollinearity from that used in Equation 2, and the last bei
based on all census tracts for which data were available.

Some of the variables, such as accessibility to shopping
areas, accessibility to industrial areas, and crime rate,
proved to be insignificant in helping explain variations in property values and were dropped from the final equations. But
the variables we are left with all enter in the hypothesized
way and together explain virtually all of the variance in property
values. Most important, the air-pollution variable, sulfation,
turns out to add a significant amount to the over-all explanation.
Using Equation 2 and judging in terms of beta coefficients,
sulfation is almost as important as accessibility to highways
and more important than RILL, time zones, and school quality.
A linear fit appears to be best, and a value for the partial regression coefficient of -\$245 per sulfation zone, which is sig-
nificantly different from zero at the 0.3 per cent level, is
reasonably well supported by the alternative estimates for
this coefficient presented in Table 14. The hypothesis that
property values are adversely affected by pollution, other effects held constant, appears fully warranted by our evidence.

The partial regression coefficient for sulfation in Table 14
can be interpreted as meaning that if the sulfation levels to
which any single-family dwelling unit is exposed were to drop
by 0.25 mg of $SO_3/100cm^2/day$, the value of that property can
be expected to rise by at least \$83 and more likely closer to
\$245. Assuming no offsetting market adjustments, this con-

clusion can be generalized to all houses in the St. Louis metropolitan area. Table 15 presents several such total estimates. The first and third columns present figures representing the extent to which property values might rise if sulfation levels throughout the city were reduced by 0.25 mg of SO_3/100cm^2/day, but in no case below 0.49 mg , which we take as the background level. The second two columns indicate what might happen if sulfation were reduced to a uniform 0.49 mg level. The other entries in the table should be self-explanatory. To indicate the annual cost that is incurred because pollution levels are not at these lower levels, these figures must be multiplied by a rate of interest that reflects what could have been earned from investing these amounts. For example, using a figure of 6 per cent to reflect the mortgage borrowing rate, and assuming that the $245 loss figure is correct and that pollution levels can actually be reduced by 0.25 mg but not below 0.49 mg, we obtain an annual loss estimate for the whole St. Louis area of almost $5 million. Alternatively if a 10 per cent rate is used to reflect the average rate of return on private capital, the figure becomes $8.3 million per year.

Currently available data do not permit a careful comparison between these benefits and the costs of bringing about such a reduction. A crude assessment suggests that a shift to low sulfur fuels could cut sulfation levels roughly in half and would cost $10-$15 million per year.[24] This is a larger cut than envisioned in the above estimates, but extrapolating to this level would bring the annual benefit figure up to perhaps $15 million. However, three other considerations must be borne in mind. First, property values other than those for single-family dwell-

---

[24]Conversation with Dr. Bernard Steigerwald, Robert A. Taft Sanitary Engineering Center, Cincinnati. Other methods such as stack-cleaning processes might prove to be more economical.

Table 15

ESTIMATES OF INCREASES IN PROPERTY VALUES
FOR GIVEN REDUCTIONS IN SULFATION LEVELS

| | Partial Regression Coefficient for SUL (SUL in units of 0.25 mg. of SO_3/ 100 cm^2/day) | | | |
| | $82.97 | | $245 | |
Reduction in SO_3:	By 0.25 mg. but not below 0.49 mg.	To uniform 0.49 mg. level	By 0.25 mg. but not below 0.49 mg.	To uniform 0.49 mg. level
Total Single-Family Units in Sample	$24,393,000	$74,219,000	$72,030,000	$219,158,000
Total Single-Family Units in St. Louis SMSA [a]	28,037,000	85,150,000	82,790,000	251,437,000

[a] Assuming that tracts not in the sample have sulfation levels of between 0.75 and 0.99 mg. of

ing units would also rise, adding substantially to the above benefit estimate. Second, other benefits besides the increase in property values would also be derived from such a reduction. Third, to bring about these property-value and other benefits, it is probably necessary to reduce the levels of other pollutants (especially particulates) that are correlated with SO_3 levels, and this would substantially raise the cost estimates. Considerable work remains before an adequate comparison between the benefits and costs can be accomplished.

Finally, a word should be added about the attempts made in the household survey, summarized in Chapter 4, to determine what is being discounted in property values. This information is important in order to lend weight to the findings of this chapter, as well as to avoid double counting when property-value effects are added together with cost estimates based on other measurement strategies. While the evidence is not conclusive, it suggests that a significant number of persons in each of the sample areas do recognize that air-pollution problems differ in different parts of the city and that they associate these problems with dirt, soot, and odors.[25] There is no indication that people believe that maintenance costs (for example, painting costs) or effects on vegetation or health can be influenced by moving. These findings should be treated as tentative only, first because the poor quality of responses to many of the other questions throws some suspicions on the whole questionnaire, and second, because this evidence does not come from St. Louis

---

[25]For example, the first six questions of the questionnaire presented in Appendix D ask respondents to discuss the advantages and disadvantages of their neighborhood relative to others in the metropolitan area. Most responses to these open-ended questions pertain to other neighborhood characteristics, but 15 per cent in the heavily polluted area spontaneously indicated that a disadvantage of their neighborhood relative to others is the higher level of dirt, soot, and odor, whereas only 2 per cent in the clean area responded in this way.

where data for this property-value study were gathered. More evidence must accumulate before one can safely apply the results obtained from one city to another. Nevertheless, these results are quite encouraging and should stimulate further work along these lines.

CHAPTER **7** PROPERTY VALUES
AND AIR POLLUTION:
A TIME-SERIES
STUDY

This chapter demonstrates a method of applying time-series data to estimate the effects of air pollution on property values. As a rule, time-series analyses of the costs of air pollution are not feasible because pollution levels do not vary significantly from one year to the next and because records seldom extend far enough into the past to show significant variation. In addition, there are seldom enough data on other variables that might contribute to the observed variations in property values. However, it is sometimes possible to find special situations in which a locality experiences a relatively rapid shift in its normal level of pollution. If a suitable control area is available, such episodes permit the observation of temporal changes in property values associated with pollution. A case meeting these criteria reasonably well forms the basis of this chapter.

BACKGROUND AND METHOD OF APPROACH

During 1962, residents of a quiet, middle-class neighborhood in south St. Louis began to complain about the choking gases from a plant that had just been taken over by a metal fabricating firm. The odors were described in a petition to the city of St. Louis on behalf of 270 residents as nauseous, causing "headaches, smarting of the eyes and injury to the respiratory system and loss of appetite."[1] There had been no

---

[1]Petition on file in the Office of the Air Pollution Commissioner of St. Louis.

previous complaints about the quality of the air in this neighborhood, although 17 per cent of the census tract from which
the petitions came had been devoted to industrial use for several years. In August of 1963 hearings were held on the
matter but no public action resulted. In June of 1965 a second
set of hearings was held following which the company was de-
clared a public nuisance by the Air Pollution Commissioner of
St. Louis in accordance with the city's air-pollution ordinance.
The company immediately appealed, an action that permitted
it to continue its previous operations without penalty until
a decision was reached on its appeal. The appeal hearings
took place in June of 1966, and at this writing no decision has
yet been reached. Although the company has taken some measures to alleviate the situation, residents of the area claim
that the effect has been negligible. The situation is apparently
worst during spring and summer, partly due to open windows
and partly to the seasonal nature of the company's business.
Apart from this seasonal fluctuation, therefore, pollution level
in this area appears to have remained at a new, higher level
from 1962 to the present.

To assess the effect of pollution on property values in this
neighborhood (apart from changes in general market conditions
that also occur over time), a control area was selected which
was as similar as possible to the affected area. Indexes of re-
corded sales of property in the two areas were then compared
to determine the independent effect of the pollution.

The affected area is defined as the downwind portions of
census tract 15C, an area slightly larger than that within
which lived those who signed the petition. (See Figure 8.) The
effect of air pollution is unlikely to have extended beyond the
boundaries of tract 15C. The control area is defined as the
remainder of tract 15C, except for commercial and industrial
areas, plus census tract 15A which lies almost immediately
west (and upwind) of the affected area. Tract 15A was selected after it was compared with the whole of tract 15C using
available statistical information and personal observations of
the area. Table 16 presents the statistical comparison.

Figure 8
CENSUS TRACT 15C, ST. LOUIS

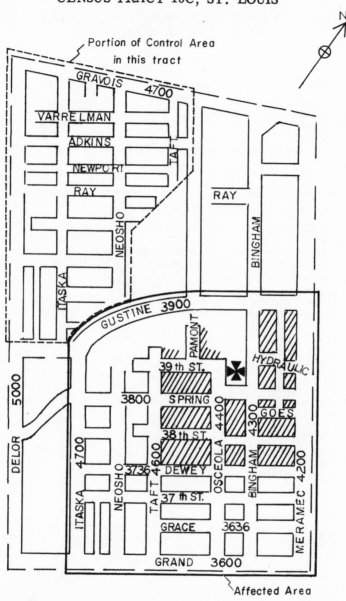

✠ Pollution Source

▨ Blocks from which petitions were obtained

143

Table 16

PROPERTY VALUES AND SELECTED CHARACTERISTICS OF
CENSUS TRACTS 15A and 15C

	Tract 15A	Tract 15C
GENERAL CHARACTERISTICS [a]		
Total Population	4,647	6,367
Median Property Value	$11,700	$12,100
Median Gross Rent	$76	$78
Median Income of Families and Unrelated Individuals	$5,713	$6,010
Median Number of Rooms	4.6	4.6
Per Cent Blue-Collar Workers	40%	38%
LABOR-FORCE CHARACTERISTICS [b]		
Labor-Force Distribution, % :		
Total Civilian Labor Force	2,010	2,792
Professional, Technical, and Kindred Workers	7	10
Managers, Officers, and Proprietors	7	5
Clerical and Kindred Workers	27	26
Sales Workers	8	8
Craftsmen, Kindred Workers, Foremen	16	16
Operatives and Kindred Workers	20	18
Private Household Workers	1	0
Service Workers	8	5
Laborers, Except Mine	3	3
Occupation Not Reported	2	4
AGE [b]		
Age Distribution, %:		
Under 5 Years	8	8
5 to 14 Years	15	17
15 to 24 Years	11	12
25 to 44 Years	20	22
45 to 64 Years	32	29
65 Years and Over	18	13
Median Age, Years:		
Male	40.3	36.2
Female	44.8	40.0
HOUSING [b]		
Number of Housing Units	1,638	2,096
Age Distribution of Units, %:		
Built 1950 to 1960	2	7
Built 1940 to 1949	1	6
Built 1939 or earlier	97	87

Table 16

(Continued)

	Tract 15A	Tract 15C
Condition of Units, %:		
Sound	93	97
Deteriorating	7	2
Dilapidated	0	0
Per Cent of Units in Single-Family Housing Units	73	71
Per Cent of Units Vacant and Available for Sale or Rent	1.5	1.5
LAND USE CHARACTERISTICS, % of total acres		
Total Residential	41	36
One-Family	37	30
Two-Family	2	4
Three- and Four-Family	1	1
Public and Semipublic	4	9
Commercial	7	2
Industrial	15	17
Streets and Alleys	30	25
Vacant	1	9
ACCESSIBILITY[e]		
Time to Central Business District by Bus	23 min.	23 min.

[a]Source: U.S. Bureau of the Census, U.S. Census of Population and Housing: 1960, Census Tracts, Final Report PHC (1) - B1 (Washington, D.C.: U.S. Government Printing Office, 1962); and David J. Pittman and Sarah L. Boggs, "An Analysis of Population, Housing, Crime and Delinquency Characteristics in the Study Area, " Juvenile Delinquency Planning Grant, Project of St. Louis, 1963, mimeo.

[b]Calculated from U.S. Bureau of the Census, U.S. Census of Population and Housing: 1960, Census Tracts, Final Report PHC (1) - B1 (Washington, D. C.: U.S. Government Printing Office, 1962).

[c]Of this number, 1,068 units fall into the affected area.

[d]Calculated from St. Louis City Planning Commission, St. Louis Land Use Statistics, 1963.

[e]Estimated from St. Louis Public Service route schedules.

The physical characteristics of tract 15C include a relatively small industrial development running north and south
diagonally through the tract but only two city blocks in width.
A railroad line runs directly behind and parallel to the industrial area. Most of the residential properties are on low
ground beginning at the eastern edge of the industrial development and going eastward. At the southeastern edge of the
tract along Delor Street, a new shopping center was built in
1962. Directly west of the center, new middle-income, three-
story apartment buildings were built in 1962 and early 1964.[2]

Both the physical appearance and the relevant housing market statistics of census tract 15A appear to be comparable to
those of census tract 15C.[3] There is even an industrial development along its western edge of roughly comparable size.
Yet this tract is sufficiently far from the pollution source so
as not to be affected by the pollutants that affected tract 15C.

RESULTS AND INTERPRETATION

Since comprehensive data on property values are available
only for the census year 1960, public records of actual transactions were used to construct indexes of changes in property
values for the period 1957 through 1965. Two different indexes
were applied to the same set of data. The most desirable of
the two is the regression index; the second, included for comparison purposes because it is in more common use, is the
median index.[4] Methods of constructing these indexes are
presented in Appendix G.

------

[2] The apartments are described as attractive though they
add somewhat to conjestion in the area.

[3] The boundaries of census tract 15A are Morganford Avenue on the east, Eichelberger Avenue on the south, Kingshighway Avenue on the west, and Chippewa Avenue on the north.

[4] The regression index makes use of more information and
uses least-squares methods to minimize unexplained variance
in the data. See Appendix G and footnote reference cited there

If the two areas are comparable, the indexes for the affected and control areas should portray similar variations up to 1962, so that any divergence after that date can reasonably be expected to reflect the effects of pollution alone. Table 17 and Figure 9 present the relevant information for examining such changes. Visual inspection suggests a reasonable, though not striking, degree of conformity between the indexes for the two areas prior to 1962. Except for 1959 and 1960, tests of statistical significance tend to support the hypothesis that there is no significant difference between them. No explanation for the unexpected divergence in the indexes during 1959 and 1960 has been found.

Accepting the basic comparability of the two areas, the pollution emitted from 1962 on should create a relative decline in property values in the affected area. This gap should widen for a time and then stabilize until the pollution problem has abated. Judging from the annual figures, this appears to have been the case in 1963 and 1964. Indeed, the regression index, the more reliable of the two, indicates statistically significant differences for these two years; and the average difference after 1962 is greater than that for 1962 and earlier.

After 1964, however, the gap narrows. If this trend were to continue into 1966 with no change in pollution, our conclusions might not stand. However, the half-year figures, available for the median index, suggest that this is unlikely. Apparently, the narrowing of the gap results from a temporary jump in values in the affected area and a drop in values in the control area during the first half of 1965. The index for the affected area during the second half of 1965 is again significantly below that of the control area.

No adequate explanation for these recent sharp, temporary shifts is apparent. It is possible that construction in the two areas has led to some instability in property values, that the continuous, absolute decline in the affected area from 1962 to the middle of 1964 was an overreaction which led to a brief period of overcorrection, or that these movements reflect

Table 17

MEDIAN AND REGRESSION INDEXES OF PROPERTY VALUES, 1957-65

Year	Median Index			Regression Index			Number of Sales	
	Affected Area	Control Area	P^a	Affected Area	Control Area	P^a	Affected Area	Control Area
1957	100	100	--	100	100	--	48	97
1958	95.4	99.9	.40	95.8	94.3	.75	31	77
1959	95.7	112.1	.001	95.8	105.4	.01	38	87
1960	101.3	112.3	.02	101.6	109.3	.03	35	72
1961	99.6	101.7	.76	96.4	101.2	.40	20	65
1962	100.5	102.0	.86	94.6	97.5	.50	31	63
1963	90.2	95.0	.41	90.6	99.1	.04	35	69
1964: 1st half	(83.0)	(105.0)					(16)	(22)
2nd half	(100.9)	(119.3)					(16)	(15)
12 mos.	93.6	105.2	.18	91.8	106.6	.001	32	37
1965: 1st half	(113.7)	(103.4)					(15)	(15)
2nd half	(99.6)	(116.4)					(15)	(17)
12 mos.	106.8	110.7	.57	102.3	107.8	.30	30	32

[a]P is the probability that the observed difference between the index values for the affected and control areas for a given year is due to sampling error (two-tailed test). The null hypothesis under test here is that the true difference is zero.

Figure 9

MEDIAN AND REGRESSION INDEXES OF
PROPERTY VALUES, 1957-65

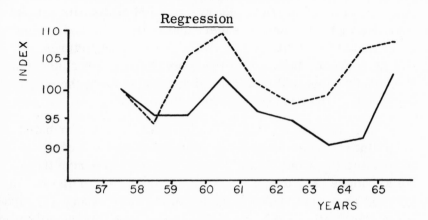

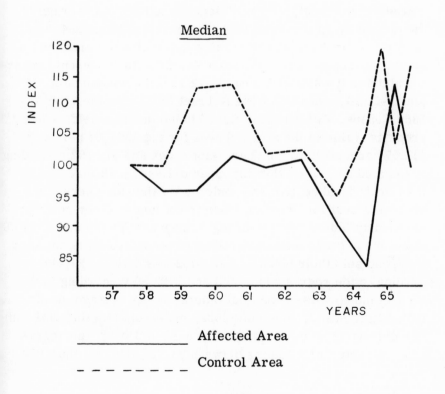

changing hopes concerning legal actions under way against the plant. These movements could also be fortuitous, related to a few special sales. Detailed investigation of the data and discussions with community leaders and real-estate and air-pollution experts failed to indicate which of these conjectures, if any, is correct. But none of these possibilities precludes the presumption that pollution caused at least some of the observed gap between the two indexes after 1962.

To the extent that property-value losses can be attributed to air pollution, those losses will be indicated more clearly by translating them into dollar terms. One way to derive these dollar values is to assume that, in the absence of pollution, the affected area would have experienced the same changes in property values after 1962 as did the control area. If the difference in the indexes for 1962 are regarded as negligible (as they are on statistical grounds), it is sufficient to multiply the average of the percentage differences in the indexes for 1963, 1964, and 1965 by the average property value in the affected area during the same period. The only figure available to represent property values in the affected area is $12,100, the median value of single-family houses in Census Tract 15C, available from the 1960 Census. Applying this figure to the indexes yields a mean property value in the affected area for the 1963-65 period of $11,574 according to the regression index and $11,302 according to the median index. Now the mean percentage differences in the affected and control area indexes for the same period are 10.12 per cent for the regression index and 6.91 per cent for the median index. The resulting figures are $1,144 and $799.80. Thus, the average loss incurred by homeowners in the affected area who sold their houses after 1962 was between $1,144 (according to the regression index) and $799.80 (according to the median index). Assuming that others, on the average, would have had to sustain this same loss, and estimating the total number of housing units in the affected area at 1,068,[5] the aggregate property-value loss is between $1,222,000 and $854,000.

---

[5]See footnote c to Table 16.

Obviously, a great many assumptions underly the foregoing calculations -- so many that little confidence can be placed in the final results. The control area is not an ideal representation of what would have happened in the affected area in the absence of pollution, as implied by the unexplained divergencies between their indexes in 1959 and 1960. We do not know whether any of the explanations for the sharp, temporary shifts in the indexes during the first half of 1965 are correct. In particular, we do not know whether the observed values are equilibrium values -- that is, whether they represent the full effect on property values or an over- or underreaction. Finally, it must be remembered that no objective, numerical assessment of the extent of the pollution introduced after 1962 is available; this is unfortunate because without such a measure it is difficult to assess the reasonableness of the alleged effects.

Perhaps additional data beyond 1965 can clarify the situation. If, for example, property values in the affected area rise relative to those in the control area after pollution is eliminated, the case would be considerably stronger. As things stand now, the principal value of the study lies not in the numerical findings, which could easily be proved wrong by additional data, but in illustrating the time-series approach and its difficulties.

CHAPTER **8** SOME LESSONS FOR
FUTURE RESEARCH

At the outset of this study it was suggested that quantitative economic studies of air pollution be directed toward the long-range goal of specifying adequate air-quality standards and appropriate control measures. For this purpose two hypothetical curves relating pollution to economic variables were described: a cost-of-pollution curve and a cost-of-control curve. This study has been concerned with only one of these, the cost-of-pollution curve. Its purpose has been to develop and wherever possible to test methods for estimating this curve for specific pollutants and localities, and to indicate the assumptions and limitations of the methods as a guide to both producer and consumers of such data. Given this focus, the principal value of the study is to be found in the chapters themselves, rather than in the more general findings that can be discussed in conclusion. But having been through these exercises, it is useful to look back over the terrain from a hopefully new perspective. This chapter will consider briefly the progress made here toward developing cost-of-pollution curves, what needs to be done to extend and improve these methods, and what future research strategy should be followed.

Each of the measurement studies has been identified as an application of one of the general strategies for measurement developed in Chapter 2. It will be helpful to consider their merits and limitations for future research in terms of these strategies.

THE COST OF POLLUTION IN THE
ABSENCE OF ADJUSTMENTS

To construct a cost-of-pollution curve on the basis of the
first strategy (which disregards individual adjustments), three
inputs are necessary: a damage function indicating the quantitative relationship between specific air pollutants and specific
losses in economic function, a monetary price to represent
the cost of a unit of damage, and an indication of the number of
units at risk. Chapter 3 demonstrated an ability to provide information on unit costs in the difficult and sensitive area of
human health. It would not be difficult, especially in this area,
to provide information on the population at risk by broadly
specified pollution zones. But since adequate damage functions
are absent, it is impossible to develop cost-of-pollution curves
with this information.[1]

The inability to apply this strategy is unfortunate, for in
relation to certain categories of cost, it is potentially the most
promising of the three strategies. In the first place, experimental methods can be used to develop many of the damage
functions. In contrast to other strategies, this means substantially greater ability to control for the effects of other factors
which also cause the same damage, an especially important
characteristic in an area where the effect we are trying to
measure is likely to be small relative to other contributing
factors. In addition, the application of this strategy would
capture the principal costs of the pollution in one figure before
these costs are spread among various goods and services purchased in an attempt to cope with the damage. This, of course,
is also its chief weakness, for just because it does not allow
for adjustments meant to minimize the direct damage, it tends

---

[1]A crude assessment of costs due to air pollution, however,
can be derived,as in Chapter 3, by attributing to air pollution
the difference between urban and rural disease rates after adjustment for known nonpollution factors.

to overstate the costs of pollution. In those areas where there
is little opportunity to adjust, and especially for effects
amenable to study by experimental methods, this may be a
small price to pay for the greater confidence obtained from
the answers.

Because of the advantages inherent in this first approach
we have tried to find ways to extend experimental methods into
areas involving individual adjustments. Toward this end a
proposal for a somewhat novel set of experiments was set forth
at the end of Chapter 4. While this method is likely to be appropriate in only limited areas (principally in cases concerned
with soiling and materials damage) its advantages over other
methods warrant its serious consideration.

STUDIES INVOLVING INDIVIDUAL ADJUSTMENTS

The second strategy of measurement recognizes that individuals can and do adjust in many ways to minimize their losses
from air pollution. Indeed, this inclination to adjust is why
experimental approaches lead to overestimates of the cost of
pollution. The difficulty here is that no single method of estimating such adjustments will suffice; instead, special tactics
geared to the peculiarities of each mode of adjustment must be
devised. Chapters 4 and 5 are aimed at this task.

Chapter 4 discusses a series of studies all of which led to
negative findings. One thing these studies have in common is
their reliance upon differences in normally experienced levels
of air pollution, and it may well be that these differences are
simply not great enough to generate observed behavioral
differences. But at least in some of these studies there are
other reasons operating as well, several of which are relevant
for future work in this area.

First, it seems clear that quantitative research on air-pollution problems cannot rely on statistical materials gathered for
other purposes. Although the total effect of pollution may be
large, it can manifest itself in a wide variety of small ways.

Without data that reflect these small but numerous effects --
data from the specific geographic areas for which there are
good air-pollution measurements -- the differential effect of
pollution is likely to be lost "in the noise."

Second, household surveys intended to gather such data
must be designed with great care, in great detail, and with
considerably greater sophistication than current techniques
will afford. The results of Chapter 5 demonstrate the feasi-
bility of this approach, at least in cases where pollution levels
temporarily rise far above normal, but even here the variances
in the responses are large. In applications to areas with more
common differences in air-pollution levels, the type of questionnaires used in this study is inadequate. A substantially
more detailed and psychologically sophisticated instrument
must be developed for this purpose. But the development of
such techniques is likely to involve basic research into questions relating to the formation of perceptions and attitudes --
fields that are far removed from the air-pollution problems
and questions that are unlikely to be answered in the near
future.

The inadequacy of available techniques is particularly apparent where willingness-to-pay questions are involved.
While statistically significant differences in responses to these
questions were obtained from the household questionnaire of
Chapter 4, we have insufficient evidence to know what people
mean by their responses. Furthermore, the failure of the behavioral questions to measure direct costs prohibits the estimation of psychic costs as a residual, a procedure suggested
in Chapter 2. The little evidence available in Chapter 5 on this
score suggests that there may be a small group of persons
who can understand and correctly respond to these questions;
but it is probably not legitimate to generalize from them to the
rest of the population. On the whole, therefore, we are unable
to provide answers to the questions raised about this approach
in Chapter 2. To do so would probably require a study at
least as large and detailed as this one.

Third, some of the negative findings could have resulted from inadequate or inappropriate air-pollution data. Considering the complexity of the problem, there are actually very few measurements available. It is common, for example, to find information on the weight of particulate matter, but not on the number of particles and their composition, though these characteristics may be more important.[2] Adequate evidence is not available to indicate which statistical measures of frequency intensity, and duration of exposure are most relevant for studies of physical and economic effects of pollution. More emphasis needs to be placed on acids, oxidants, oxides of nitrogen, and on groups of pollutants that act together.

Moreover, much more information is needed by smaller and more carefully selected geographic units. The National Air Sampling Network consists of one downtown collection station in each of over 200 cities. Since variations in pollution levels within metropolitan areas are often greater than variations among cities, the whole area can seldom be represented by this single station.[3] Even fixed outdoor stations in different parts of the city may be inadequate to represent the quality of the environment in which the typical urban dweller lives. Pollution levels inside apartments and closed automobiles may be substantially different from -- indeed, sometimes higher than -- those of the outside environment.

---

[2] Big particles do not get into the lungs as easily as small, and particulates to which sulfuric acid molecules are attached are more damaging than those to which no acid is attached. But measurements by weight cannot distinguish these cases.

[3] It has been suggested that data from this one station can be combined with dispersion models to obtain an adequate picture of the pollution pattern within a city. The experience reflected in Chapters 5 and 6 does not allow for much optimism on this score.

Finally, there remains the inherent difficulty of identifying and holding constant all the other factors that could also explain the observed behavior. Habit, personality differences, the extent to which buildings are sealed from the outside atmosphere, changes in taste, and the like are difficult, if not impossible, to cope with outside of an experimental setting. It is principally for this reason, but also because of the problems with the interview approach, that the proposal to extend the use of experimental methods are made.

PROPERTY VALUE STUDIES

The third strategy of measurement seeks to measure economic costs by observing price differentials in the real-estate market that can be attributed to air pollution. Since in theory such price differentials can capture in one figure all the costs of pollution specific to the property, including psychic costs, it is an attractive approach. The cross-section study presented in Chapter 6 is very encouraging in that it proved possible to develop a model that satisfies most statistical criteria and yields estimates which (with certain qualifications) can be interpreted as the slope of the cost-of-pollution curve for this category of effects. Chapter 7 demonstrates a procedure for obtaining similar material from time-series information.

Clearly these studies should be pursued further. The cross-section study should be repeated in other cities; a more detailed study should be undertaken using observations in the same study area to determine just what is being discounted in these property values; there may be value in additional work to find ways to reduce the bias inherent in the interpretation of the findings; and if and when they become available, time-series data should be used in conjunction with the cross-section materials. If these studies continue to yield positive results, more detailed work -- using a finer breakdown of pollution levels, units smaller than census tracts, land values rather than property values, and so forth -- would be justified.

Within the conceptual framework of this study, two types of research priorities can be discussed. The first involves priorities among the various measurement strategies discussed in this volume, and the second is based on the merits of any of these studies as compared with investigations that are also necessary for standard setting and control purposes.

With regard to the studies described here, it is clear that property-value studies should be pursued further, but with a clear perception of the need to determine just what is being discounted in them. Unless this is known accurately, the results will lack credence and there is a risk of double counting when property-value effects are combined with other types of cost information. High priority should also be given to extending experimental methods into new areas, as proposed in Chapter 4, and in general to developing direct damage functions. But survey methods are doubtful techniques, at least in the soiling and material damage areas. They are likely to be very costly, and since a number of basic methodological problems must be resolved in order to obtain useful results, the probability of failure must be considered high. A very high value must be placed on the numerical results in order to justify such an effort.

Whatever the priorities among these attempts to establish cost-of-pollution curves, they must be considered in conjunction with attempts to establish the other set of curves described in Chapter 1: the cost-of-control curves, which have not been discussed here at all. If a cost-of-control schedule -- that is, a list of least-cost methods of achieving different air-quality standards -- were available, pollution standards could be set simply by asking legislators which standard they are willing to support financially. This is a judgment that these men must make no matter how much information is available on the cost-of-pollution damage.

Of course, the measurement problems may be just as severe here as on the cost-of-pollution side. Alternative ways to achieve different target levels for certain key pollutants

would have to be sought, and for each, estimates of the costs
(and other consequences) of accepting each alternative must
be developed. These tasks would require cooperation among
many specialists, especially the engineer, the city planner, and
the economist, and -- just as on the cost-of-pollution side --
would require the collection of considerable raw data, including
some pertaining to attitudes and behavioral changes. But
these problems are not decisive. It must be remembered that
studies of the costs of control would have to be undertaken
even if adequate information on the costs of pollution were
available. Furthermore, given the virtual absence of cost-of-
control studies comparable to this one on pollution damage,
there is little basis on which to judge the difficulties that may
arise.

Admittedly, without an estimate of the pollution costs, the
policy-maker must base his decision solely on his assessment
of the financial burden the electorate will bear; and given their
ignorance of pollution costs, they are likely to prefer too low
a standard. As an interim solution, reliance on the legislator
may not be at all undesirable. Since elected representatives,
more than any other segment of our society, are attuned to the
attitudes that form psychic costs, and since psychic costs are
likely to be a large portion of total costs, their assessment may
not be too far from the mark. In any event, given the experience
of this study, there may be no other solution available for some
time to come.

But it can only be an interim solution. For without an adequate knowledge of the effects of pollution, the legislator can
do nothing but reflect his constituents' attitudes: He cannot --
nor can we -- argue for a more reasonable standard.

APPENDIXES

APPENDIX A
EVALUATION OF HOUSEWIFE SERVICES*

Of women fourteen years of age and over, only 35 per cent are in the labor force. Except for the younger ages, the others are mainly housewives, and standard national accounting procedures impute no value to their services. It is obvious that women produce certain services in the home that should be counted as output, and which would be lost if the woman in the house were to die from some disease. But it is difficult to know how to estimate the value of this output. One procedure that has been suggested and used is to estimate the value of a woman's services as the value of a maid living in the home, adjusted for the number of "responsibility units" (persons in the household) she cares for.[1] While quite ingenious and suggestive of what might be done with better data, this procedure introduces arbitrary assumptions that make it difficult to judge the direction, as well as the size, of the errors involved.

First, the housewife does not spend the same number of hours a day working as would a domestic servant. In some cases, many more hours may be spent, though perhaps less efficiently. In other cases, particularly if she has a full-time maid, the housewife may spend her day as a consumer rather than a producer. In fact, instead of equating her economic value to that of a domestic servant, it could be argued that it should be equated to the value of what she consumes, on the ground that her productive services must be "worth" at least

---

*See Chapter 3.

[1]Weisbrod, op.cit., pp. 114-18.

that much to the head of the household. However, this approach
entails imputing a value to the leisure time she "consumes,"
and in any case is only valid if the head of the household had
the choice of reducing her consumption in case she did not provide "equivalent" value in productive services.

Second, since there is no direct information concerning the
age of women by family size, Weisbrod assumed that the housewife is three years younger than the head of the household.
This adjustment was made for all household units, even though
for some the housewife is also the head.

Third, while the attempt to adjust the value of a housewife's
services for the number of responsibility units is a move in the
right direction, it is important to take into account the age of
these units. Children and adults of different ages require services of the houswife that can have radically different values.
At one time the woman may be providing baby-sitting services
and an informal education for her children; at another time
she may be providing home-nursing services for an older member of the household. Unfortunately, data limitations make it
impossible to take this factor into account.

These considerations led us to reject Weisbrod's method,
even though we have nothing better to substitute. To obtain
better estimates, a detailed study of housewife services would
have to be undertaken, somewhat along the lines attempted for
cleaning chores in Chapter 4. Such an investigation was beyond
the scope of this study.

APPENDIX B
DETAILED TABLES FOR CHAPTER 3

Table 1

PRESENT VALUE OF FUTURE EARNINGS
BY AGE AND SEX FOR THE YEAR 1960

| Age | Discount Rate of .05 | | Discount Rate of .10 | |
	Males	Females	Males	Females
10	$42,834	$12,139	$14,720	$ 4,441
11	44,994	12,750	16,119	4,886
12	47,264	13,391	17,826	5,377
13	49,653	14,065	19,619	5,916
14	52,146	14,769	21,571	6,505
15	54,720	15,481	23,671	7,126
16	57,318	16,175	25,869	7,755
17	59,800	16,809	28,035	8,351
18	62,157	17,230	30,163	8,762
19	64,342	17,472	32,210	9,014
20	66,390	17,636	34,212	9,202
21	68,266	17,738	36,136	9,336
22	69,676	17,794	37,690	9,434
23	70,918	17,865	39,159	9,552
24	71,901	17,965	40,455	9,709
25	72,571	18,087	41,519	9,897
26	72,957	18,241	42,375	10,130
27	73,143	18,408	43,098	10,390
28	73,063	18,565	43,620	10,659
29	72,673	18,711	43,889	10,936
30	72,145	18,834	44,066	11,209
31	71,429	18,193	44,099	11,459
32	70,523	18,927	43,982	11,666
33	69,444	18,878	43,724	11,828
34	68,246	18,763	43,374	11,943
35	66,934	18,556	42,932	11,982
36	65,529	18,292	42,418	11,980
37	64,038	17,946	41,834	11,907
38	62,483	17,512	41,199	11,757
39	60,864	17,012	40,512	11,546
40	59,177	16,418	39,766	11,245
41	57,430	15,775	38,968	10,894
42	55,638	15,136	38,129	10,543
43	53,784	14,459	37,229	10,152
44	51,881	13,794	36,282	9,767
45	49,921	13,128	35,274	9,375
46	47,906	12,462	34,207	8,977
47	45,836	11,822	33,077	8,600

Table 1 (Continued)

Age	Discount Rate of . 05		Discount Rate of . 10	
	Males	Females	Males	Females
48	43,712	11,205	31,830	8,240
49	41,587	10,569	30,666	7,854
50	39,411	9,947	29,381	7,477
51	37,231	9,300	28,073	7,068
52	35,001	8,653	26,690	6,651
53	32,753	8,000	25,264	6,220
54	30,490	7,315	23,796	5,746
55	28,154	6,651	22,227	5,280
56	25,776	6,006	20,583	4,821
57	23,419	5,357	18,920	4,345
58	21,058	4,703	17,210	3,851
59	18,669	4,072	15,425	3,362
60	16,293	3,469	13,600	2,886
61	13,969	2,907	11,768	2,433
62	11,685	2,411	9,917	2,030
63	9,495	1,985	8.094	1,681
64	7,512	1,603	6,413	1,365
65	6,146	1,310	5,284	1,125
66	5,047	1,059	4,383	918
67	4,056	847	3,559	743
68	3,197	658	2,838	584
69	2,429	486	2,183	436
70	1,746	348	1,590	317
71	1,178	231	1,089	213
72	692	134	651	125
73	246	58	235	25
74	-	-	-	-

Source: Calculated from formula given in text. Labor force participation rates were taken from U.S. Bureau of the Census, U.S. Census of the Population: 1960, Subject Reports, Employment Status and Work Experience, Final Report PC(2)-6A (Washington, D.C.: U.S. Government Printing Office, 1963), p. 1. Life expectancy was computed from U.S. Department of Health, Education and Welfare, Vital Statistics of the U.S., 1960, Vol. II, Section 2, Life Tables (Washington, D.C.: Public Health Service, 1960), pp. 2-9. Earnings by age were estimated from data in U.S. Census of Population: 1960, Subject Reports, Occupational Characteristics, Final Report PC(2)-7A, pp. 416-444. Median earnings for 1959 by age and profession were weighted by the number of employed individuals in the labor force of that age and profession to obtain the average earnings for any given age. The earnings were reported by age category and the data had to be hand smoothed. The estimates will be low because the earnings data include some, but not all, of those who suffered some unemployment.

Table 2

PRESENT VALUE OF LOST EARNINGS DUE TO DEATH
FROM CANCER OF THE RESPIRATORY SYSTEM

(1) Age	(2) Number of Deaths	(3) Present Value of Earnings, Using Discount Rates of :		(4) Total Loss[a]	
		.05	.10	.05	.10
a. Males					
10-14	9	$47,264	$17,826	$425,376	$160,434
15-19	11	59,800	28,035	657,800	308,385
20-24	20	69,676	37,690	1,393,520	753,800
25-29	46	73,143	43,098	3,364,578	1,982,508
30-34	148	70,523	43,982	10,437,404	6,509,336
35-39	564	64,038	41,834	36,117,432	23,594,376
40-44	859	55,638	38.129	47,793,042	32,752,811
45-49	1,797	45,836	33,077	82,367,292	59,439,369
50-54	3,251	35,001	26,690	113,788,251	86,769,190
55-59	4,515	23,419	18,920	105,736,785	85,423,800
60-64	5,776	11,685	9,917	67,492,560	57,280,592
65-69	5,753	4,056	3,559	23,334,168	20,474,927
70-74	4,015	692	651	2,778,380	2,613,765
Total	26,564			495,686,588	378,063,293
Average				18,660	14,232
b. Females					
10-14	6	13,391	5,377	80,346	32,262
15-19	6	16,809	8,351	100,854	50,106
20-24	4	17,794	9,434	71,176	37,736
25-29	16	18,408	10,390	294,528	166,240
30-34	51	18,927	11,666	965,277	594,966
35-39	142	17,946	11,907	2,548,332	1,690,794
40-44	253	15,136	10,543	3,829,408	2,667,379
45-49	399	11,822	8,600	4,716,978	3,431,400
50-54	498	8,653	6,651	4,309,194	3,312,198
55-59	553	5,357	4,345	2,962,421	2,402,785
60-64	662	2,441	2,030	1,596,082	1,343,660
65-69	765	847	743	647,955	568,395
70-74	726	134	125	97,284	90,750
Total	4,081			22,219,835	16,388,871
Average				5,445	4,016

Sources: Column 2: Vital Statistics of the United States, 1958,
Vol. 2. Column 3: Data given in Table 1. The earnings values were
taken as of the midpoint of the age group.

[a]Column 2 x Column 3.

168

Table 3

PRESENT VALUE OF LOST EARNINGS DUE TO DEATH
FROM CHRONIC BRONCHITIS

(1) Age	(2) Number of Deaths	(3) Present Value of Earnings, Using Discount Rates of:		(4) Total Loss[a]	
		.05	.10	.05	.10
a. Males					
10-14	7	$47,264	$17,826	$330,848	$124,782
15-19	4	59,800	28,035	239,200	112,140
20-24	3	69,676	37,690	209,028	113,070
25-29	6	73,143	43,098	438,858	258,588
30-34	7	70,523	43,982	493,661	307,873
35-39	11	64,038	41,834	704,418	460,174
40-44	23	55,638	38,129	1,279,674	876,967
45-49	30	45,836	33,077	1,375,080	992,310
50-54		35,001	26,690	2,940,084	2,241,960
55-59	150	23,419	18,920	3,512,850	2,838,000
60-64	269	11,685	9,917	3,143,265	2,667,673
65-69	314	4,056	3,559	1,273,584	1,117,526
70-74	268	692	651	185,456	174,468
Total	1,176			16,126,006	12,285,532
Average				13,713	10,447
b. Females					
10-14	4	13,391	5,377	53,564	21,508
15-19	4	16,809	8,351	67,236	33,404
20-24	4	17,794	9,434	71,176	37,736
25-29	5	18,408	10,390	92,040	51,950
30-34	9	18,927	11,666	170,343	104,994
35-39	8	17,946	11,907	143,568	95,256
40-44	15	15,136	10,543	227,040	158,145
45-49	18	11,822	8,600	212,796	154,800
50-54	20	8,653	6,651	173,060	133,020
55-59	31	5,357	4,345	166,067	134,659
60-64	39	2,411	2,030	94,029	79,170
65-69	54	847	743	47,196	40,122
70-74	62	134	125	8,308	7,750
Total	273			1,526,423	1,052,550
Average				5,591	3,855

Source: See Table 2.

[a]Column 2 x Column 3.

Table 4

PRESENT VALUE OF LOST EARNINGS DUE TO DEATH
FROM ACUTE BRONCHITIS

(1) Age	(2) Number of Deaths	(3) Present Value of Earnings, Using Discount Rates of:		(4) Total Loss[a]	
		.05	.10	.05	.10
a. Males					
10-14	6	$47,264	$17,826	$283,584	$106,956
15-19	4	59,800	28,035	239,200	112,140
20-24	-	69,676	37,690	-	-
25-29	4	73,143	43,068	292,572	172,392
30-34	5	70,523	43,982	352,615	219,910
35-39	7	64,038	41,834	448,266	292,838
40-44	5	55,638	38,129	278,190	190,645
45-49	15	45,836	33,077	687,540	496,155
50-54	20	35,001	26,690	700,020	533,800
55-59	26	23,419	18,920	608,894	491,920
60-64	35	11,685	9,917	408,975	347,095
65-69	52	4,056	3,559	210,919	185,068
70-74	44	692	651	30,448	28,644
Total	233			4,541,223	3,177,563
Average				19,920	13,638
b. Females					
10-14	1	13,391	5,377	13,391	5,377
15-19	4	16,809	8,351	67,236	33,404
20-24	4	17,794	9,434	71,186	28,302
25-29	3	18,408	10,390	55,224	31,170
30-34	9	18,927	11,666	170,343	104,994
35-39	10	17,946	11,907	179,460	119,070
40-44	10	15,136	10,543	151,350	105,430
45-49	18	11,822	8,600	212,796	154,800
50-54	9	8,653	6,651	77,877	59,859
55-59	21	5,357	4,345	112,497	91,245
60-64	12	2,411	2,030	28,932	24,360
65-69	23	847	743	19,481	17,089
70-74	25	134	125	3,350	3,125
Total	149			1,163,123	778,225
Average				7,806	5,223

Source: See Table 2.

[a]Column 2 x Column 3.

Table 5

PRESENT VALUE OF LOST EARNINGS DUE TO DEATH
FROM EMPHYSEMA

(1) Age	(2) Number of Deaths	(3) Present Value of Earnings, Using discount rates of:		(4) Total Loss[a]	
		.05	.10	.05	.10
a. Males					
10-14	1	$47,264	$17,826	$47,264	$17,826
15-19	2	59,800	28,035	119,600	56,070
20-24	1	69,676	37,690	68,676	37,690
25-29	3	73,143	43,098	219,429	129,294
30-34	7	70,523	43,982	493,661	307,874
35-39	35	64,038	41,834	2,241,330	1,464,190
40-44	93	55,638	38,129	5,174,334	3,545,995
45-49	167	45,836	33,007	7,654,612	5.523.950
50-54	309	35,001	26,690	10,815,309	8,247,210
55-59	629	23,419	18,920	14,730,551	11,900,680
60-64	1,086	11,685	9,917	12,689,910	10,769,862
65-69	1,296	4,056	3,559	5,256,576	4,612,464
70-74	1,034	692	651	715,528	673,134
Total	4,663			60,226,780	47,286,150
Average				12,918	10,141
b. Females					
10-14	1	13,391	5,317	13,391	5,377
15-19	2	16,809	8,351	33,618	16,702
20-24	3	14,794	9,434	53,214	28,302
25-29	3	18,408	10,390	55,224	31,170
30-34	3	18,927	11,666	56,781	34,998
35-39	14	17,946	11,907	251,246	166,698
40-44	21	15,136	10,543	317,856	221,403
45-49	32	11,822	8,600	378,304	275,200
50-54	49	8,653	6,651	423,997	325,899
55-59	50	5,357	4,343	267,850	217,250
60-64	83	2,411	2,030	200,113	168,490
65-69	114	847	743	96,558	84,702
70-74	123	134	125	16,482	15,375
Total	498			2,164,632	1,591,566
Average				4,347	3,196

Source: See Table 2.

[a] Column 2 x Column 3.

Table 6

PRESENT VALUE OF LOST EARNINGS DUE TO DEATH
FROM ASTHMA

(1) Age	(2) Number of Deaths	(3) Present Value of Earnings, Using Discount Rates of:		(4) Total Loss[a]	
		.05	.10	.05	.10
a. Males					
10-14	12	$47,264	$17,826	$567,168	$213,912
15-19	8	59,800	28,035	478,400	224,280
20-24	15	69,676	37,690	1,045,140	565,350
25-29	26	73,143	43,098	1,901,718	1,120,548
30-34	50	70,523	43,982	3,526,150	2,199,100
35-39	49	64,038	41,834	3,137,862	2,049,866
40-44	95	55,638	38,129	5,285,610	3,622,255
45-49	148	45,836	33,077	6,783,728	4,895,396
50-54	260	35,001	26,690	9,100,260	6,939,400
55-59	381	23,419	18,920	8,922,638	7,208,520
60-64	510	11,685	9,917	5,959,350	5,057,670
65-69	569	4,056	3,559	2,304,450	2,025,071
70-74	529	692	651	366,068	344,379
Total	2,652			49,378,543	36,465,747
Average				18,619	13,730
b. Females					
10-14	16	13,391	5,377	214,254	86,032
15-19	19	16,809	8,351	319,371	158,669
20-24	35	17,794	9,434	622,790	330,190
25-29	42	18,408	10,390	733,136	436,380
30-34	50	18,927	11,666	948,600	583,300
35-39	85	17,946	11,907	1,525,410	1,012,095
40-44	97	15,136	10,543	1,468,192	1,022,671
45-49	144	11,822	8,600	1,702,368	1,238,400
50-54	151	8,653	6,651	1,306,603	1,004,301
55-59	140	5,357	4,345	749,980	608,300
60-64	173	2,411	2,030	417,103	351,190
65-69	167	847	743	141,449	124,081
70-74	161	134	125	21,574	20,125
Total	1,280			10,170,832	6,975,734
Average				7,946	5,450
Source: See Table 2.					

[a]Column 2 x Column 3.

Table 7

PRESENT VALUE OF LOST EARNINGS DUE TO DEATH
FROM PNEUMONIA

(1) Age	(2) Number of Deaths	(3) Present Value of Earnings, Using Discount Rates of:		(4) Total Loss[a]	
		.05	.10	.05	.10
a. Males					
10-14	131	$47,264	$17,826	$6,191,584	$2,335,206
15-19	150	59,800	28,035	8,970,000	4,205,250
20-24	171	69,676	37,690	11,914,596	6,444,990
25-29	193	73,143	43,098	14,116,599	8,317,914
30-34	306	70,523	43,982	21,580,038	13,458,492
35-39	441	64,038	41,834	28,240,758	18,448,794
40-44	638	55,638	38,129	35,497,044	24,326,302
45-49	894	45,836	33,077	40,977,384	29,570,838
50-54	1,242	35,001	24,690	43,471,242	33,148,980
55-59	1,634	23,419	18,920	38,266,646	30,915,280
60-64	2,099	11,685	9,917	24,526,815	20,815,783
65-69	2,802	4,056	3,559	11,364,912	9,972,318
70-74	3,230	692	651	2,235,160	2,102,730
Total	13,931			287,352,778	204,062,877
Average				20,627	14,648
b. Females					
10-14	119	13,391	5,377	1,593,529	639,863
15-19	103	16,809	8,351	1,731,327	860,153
20-24	146	17,794	9,434	2,597,924	1,377,364
25-29	189	18,408	10,390	3,479,112	1,963,710
30-34	222	18,927	11,666	4,201,794	2,589,852
35-39	288	17,946	11,907	5,168,448	3,429,216
40-44	341	15,136	10,543	5,161,376	3,595,163
45-49	470	11,822	8,600	5,556,340	4,042,000
50-54	552	8,653	6,651	4,776,456	3,671,352
55-59	723	5,357	4,345	3,873,111	3,141,435
60-64	947	2,411	2,030	2,283,217	1,922,410
65-69	1,352	847	743	1,145,144	1,004,536
70-74	1,924	134	125	257,816	240,500
Total	7,376			41,825,594	28,477,554
Average				5,670	3,861

Source: See Table 2.

[a]Column 2 x Column 3.

Table 8

PRESENT VALUE OF POSTPONING BURIAL[a]

Age	Discount Rate of .05		Discount Rate of .10	
	Male	Female	Male	Female
0 - 1	$866	$885	$907	$916
1 - 2	889	903	930	934
2 - 3	888	902	931	935
3 - 4	886	901	931	935
4 - 5	884	900	931	935
5 - 6	882	898	930	935
7 - 8	887	894	929	935
8 - 9	874	892	928	934
9 - 10	871	890	927	934
10 - 11	868	888	926	933
12 - 13	857	880	922	931
13 - 14	857	880	922	931
14 - 15	854	877	921	941
15 - 16	846	871	918	929
16 - 17	846	871	918	929
17 - 18	842	868	917	928
18 - 19	838	865	916	927
19 - 20	834	862	915	926
20 - 21	830	858	913	925
21 - 22	826	855	912	924
22 - 23	822	851	911	923
23 - 24	817	847	909	922
24 - 25	812	843	907	921
25 - 26	807	838	906	919
26 - 27	802	834	904	918
27 - 28	796	829	901	916
28 - 29	791	824	899	914
29 - 30	784	819	896	912
30 - 31	778	814	893	910
31 - 32	771	808	890	908
32 - 33	764	803	886	905
34 - 35	749	790	878	900
35 - 36	741	784	874	897
36 - 37	733	777	869	894
37 - 38	724	770	864	891
38 - 39	715	763	859	887
39 - 40	706	756	853	883
40 - 41	697	748	847	879
41 - 42	687	740	841	875
42 - 43	677	732	827	866

[a]All estimates are below the true cost of premature burial because all those alive in their 85th year were assumed to die that year.

174

Table 8 (Continued)

Age	Discount Rate of .05		Discount Rate of .10	
	Male	Female	Male	Female
43 - 44	667	723	827	866
44 - 45	656	714	820	861
45 - 46	646	705	812	856
46 - 47	625	696	804	850
47 - 48	624	686	796	844
48 - 49	612	676	787	838
49 - 50	601	666	778	832
51 - 52	578	645	760	818
52 - 53	566	634	750	810
53 - 54	555	622	741	802
54 - 55	543	611	731	793
55 - 56	531	599	720	784
56 - 57	518	586	709	775
57 - 58	506	573	698	764
58 - 59	493	560	686	753
59 - 60	480	546	673	742
60 - 61	467	532	661	730
61 - 62	454	518	648	718
62 - 63	441	504	635	705
63 - 64	428	489	622	692
64 - 65	415	474	609	678
65 - 66	402	459	595	663
66 - 67	389	443	581	647
67 - 68	375	427	567	630
68 - 69	362	410	552	613
69 - 70	348	393	536	595
70 - 71	334	376	520	575
51 - 72	320	358	503	555
72 - 73	305	340	486	534
73 - 74	290	322	467	512
74 - 75	275	303	448	488
75 - 76	259	283	427	463
76 - 77	242	263	405	436
77 - 78	225	242	380	407
78 - 79	206	220	354	376
79 - 80	186	197	324	342
80 - 81	164	172	290	304
81 - 82	140	145	252	261
82 - 83	113	116	207	212
83 - 84	82	83	153	155
84 - 85	45	45	86	86

175

APPENDIX C
OTHER STUDIES RELATING DISEASE AND AIR POLLUTION

Several attempts were made to find materials that would permit an estimation of the number of cases of various diseases that can be attributed to air pollution. Combining this data with the unit-cost estimates of those diseases developed in this chapter would yield a first approximation to the health costs of air pollution.

MORTALITY RATES AND AIR POLLUTION

Data were gathered on mortality rates for cancer, asthma, and bronchitis for 56 different metropolitan areas that are included in the national air-sampling network. These variables were used as dependent variables in multiple regression models, using a step-wise procedure, with the following independent variables: annual geometric mean and maximum beta radioactivity levels, annual geometric mean and maximum benzene-soluble organic matter, annual geometric mean and maximum suspended particulate measurements, income per capita, population density, percentage of women, percentage of population under 18, percentage of population 55 and over, percentage nonwhite, and percentage of population living in rural farm areas of the SMSA.[1]

_____

[1]Mortality figures were taken from Vital Statistics of the United States, Vol. 2, Section 3; air-pollution data from U.S. Department of Health, Education and Welfare, Public Health Service, Air Pollution Measurements of the National Air Sampling Network (Washington, D.C.: U.S. Government Printing Office, 1962); and the remainder of the materials were obtained from selected reports of the U.S. Census of Population, all referring to 1960.

Had the regression technique yielded equations with significant coefficients of the right sign attached to the air-pollution variables, they could have been used, with the data of Chapter 2, to estimate mortality costs attributable to air pollution. However, the results were uniformly negative so far as the air-pollution variables were concerned. In only three cases were any of the pollution variables significantly different from zero around the 5 per cent level of significance; and in two of these cases the signs of the regression coefficients were negative instead of positive. The third case involved the mean of benzene-soluble organic matter which appeared to be relatively important in explaining mortalities due to asthma. However, the percentage of explained variance for the whole equation was only 23 per cent.

There are many possible reasons why this study yielded negative results. Among them is the obvious fact that data by cities are too far aggregated for this purpose, the averaging process eliminating most of the relevant variance. To improve upon this material, a search was undertaken for already gathered data within metropolitan areas where good air-pollution data are also available. Unfortunately, no data were found in a form that could be used without the expenditure of more time and money than could be afforded within the scope of this study.

ABSENTEEISM AND AIR POLLUTION

Data on absenteeism due to illness are often more readily available for small geographic areas than are mortality and morbidity statistics. While absenteeism represents only one component of the total costs of diseases, it is a significant portion and might give some clues for estimating the other components. Two attempts to utilize absenteeism records in this way were made.

The first involved the use of computer tape records provided by Union Electric Company of St. Louis for 689 employees all of whom worked in two downtown office buildings for the

whole of 1964. Both buildings are air-conditioned and sufficiently close together so that air quality can be assumed to be
the same for all individuals in the sample. After controlling
statistically for all available variables that might possibly influence the results -- wage rates, duration of employment, sick-
leave eligibility, age, marital status and sex -- the attempt was
made to determine whether absenteeism rates due to illness
could be associated with place of residence (indicated by postal
zones) and/or with sulfation rates at place of residence.

Several different definitions of absenteeism were tried.
Two definitions relate specifically to the costs that the firm
has to bear, namely, hours absent due to illness and that figure
times the appropriate wage rate for the employee; and two
other definitions increase the first two figures by an appropriate amount based on the assumption that the individual is
ill the same proportion of hours he is not paid (hours during
evenings and weekends, but not during vacations) as he is when
he is paid. Cross-classification tables and regression analysis,
using variables in both continuous and (when appropriate)
dichotomous form, were tried.

Locational variables and sulfation rates yielded insignificant
results. While this is perhaps not too surprising, especially
since the differences in air-pollution levels experienced by employees may not have been large enough to result in differences
in illness rates,[2] it is curious that the best of the regression
equations explains only 10 per cent of the observed variance in
absenteeism rates due to illness. The variables that one would
expect to be significant are only moderately so: Women are
absent almost twice as many hours as men, married more
than single; and the elderly, the newly employed, and those at

---

[2]Since pollution levels were the same for all individuals at
work, at least one fourth of the year can be assumed to have
been spent in the same environment.

the lower end of the wage scale are absent more hours than others.[3] But no explanation is available for the poor over-all quality of the equations.

The second attempt to associate absenteeism and air pollution involved the use of attendance records from elementary schools in the St. Louis metropolitan area. The rationale for this attempt was that absences from school are primarily due to illness and that this population group spends more time in a single pollution environment than any other. (Elementary school children tend to live within a few blocks of their school and are less mobile than older age groups.) Unfortunately, no controls for such variables as income or race were available which may have helped explain the negative results. No association with pollution levels was observed in the data.

---

[3]These are also the variables most often cited as explanations for differences in absenteeism rates for all causes. See Hilde Behrend, ''Voluntary Absence from Work,'' International Labor Review, February, 1959.

APPENDIX D

QUESTIONNAIRE USED IN THE HOUSEHOLD SURVEY

Daniel Yankelovich, Inc.
Philadelphia Division

Study #4046
Nov. 1965

FINAL

A STUDY OF HOUSING, CLEANING

AND MAINTENANCE

SUGGESTED INTRODUCTION: Good _____, I am _____
from Daniel Yankelovich, Inc. We are a survey organization doing a study for
a major university on housing and the maintenance and cleaning of houses.
The reason we are interested in talking to you about these things is hopefully
to contribute to making these jobs easier for homemakers.

Address: _____

Sample HH # _____   Interviewer: _____

Date: _____

Section I - Housing & Neighborhood Facts

1. Tell me about the time you moved into this house. Why did you select this neighborhood rather than some other?

2. Why did you choose this particular house rather than some other?

3. Have you ever considered moving away from this neighborhood to another section of the city?

	Yes	1
SKIP TO Q.5	No	2

4. What were the reasons for not moving?

5. What are the main advantages of living in this neighborhood?

6. What are the main disadvantages of living in this neighborhood?

7. How many years have you, yourself, lived in this house? _____ years			

13. Do you have any storm windows? Any storm doors?

		Windows	Doors
	Yes	1	1
IF BOTH NO, SKIP TO Q.15b	No	2	2

8. How many stories, above ground, is this house?

_____ stories

14. In which rooms are these storm windows and/or storm doors located? How many?

ENTER #

	Windows	Doors
Living room		
Dining room		
Master bedroom		
Other bedroom(s)		
Kitchen		
Throughout house		
Other (SPECIFY)		

9. And how many rooms does it have above ground, and not counting bathrooms?

_____ rooms

10. What is the material or materials of which the front of your house is made?

11. With what fuel is your home heated?

Coal	1
Gas	2
Oil	3
Central Plant Heat	4

12. How does this heat get up into the rooms?

Hot water through radiators	1
Hot air forced through ducts and registers	2
Other (SPECIFY)	3

15a. What reasons have you had for getting storm windows and/or storm doors?

15b. Altogether, how many windows do you have in your house?

_____ windows

185

16. Do you have any air conditioners (to cool the air) in this house?

	Yes	1
SKIP TO Q.21	No	2

17. In what room or rooms are they located?

Living room	1
Dining room	2
Master bedroom	3
Other bedroom(s)	4
Kitchen	5
Central-for whole house	6
Other (SPECIFY)	7

18. What reasons have you had for getting air conditioning?

19. About how often do you change or clean the filters in the air conditioner(s)?

Frequency _____

Never. . . . . _____

D.K. . . . . _____

20. (REFERENCE: ONLY AIR CONDITIONER OR, IF MORE THAN ONE, MOST USED AIR CONDITIONER) About how often do you use the (this) air conditioner during the summer?

Almost all the time	1
Off and on, as we like	2
Only when unbearably hot	3
Other (SPECIFY)	4

21. Do you have any air filters (to clean the air but not cool it) in this house?

	Yes	1
SKIP TO Q.23 a	No	2

22. In what room or rooms are they located?

Living room	1
Dining room	2
Master bedroom	3
Other bedroom(s)	4
Kitchen	5
Central-for whole house	6
Other (SPECIFY)	7

186

23a. Let's talk about some things that need to be done to maintain a home, like painting and papering. Regardless of who does them, about how long ago was (EACH ITEM IN TABLE BELOW) done? (RECORD IN TABLE)

23b. (WHEN LAST DONE FOR EACH ITEM) Was (ITEM) done with paid labor or unpaid labor?

24. (FOR EACH ITEM) About when might you expect to do it again (or have it done)? (RECORD IN TABLE)

Items:	Not Appli-cable	Q.23a Done Last			Q.23b When last done, done by:			Q.24 Expect Do Again		
		# Mos. Ago	# Yrs. Ago	DK	Family or Other Unpaid Labor	Paid Labor: Contract Service or Painter	Friend, Teenager, Non-Pro	# Mos. From Now	# Yrs. From Now	DK
Paint outside woodwork										
Paint front porch										
Paint outside walls										
Paint living room walls										
Paint living room woodwork										
Paint master bedroom walls										
Paint master bed-room woodwork										
Paint kitchen walls										
Paint kitchen woodwork										
Paper living room										
Paper master bedroom										
Paper kitchen										

Notes to help understand above, if needed:

25. Turning now to cleaning tasks, instead of maintenance tasks, about how often do you (EACH ITEM IN TABLE BELOW)? (RECORD IN TABLE BELOW)

26. (FOR EACH ITEM) How long did it take you to (__ITEM__) the last time you did it? (RECORD IN TABLE BELOW)

27. (FOR EACH ITEM) Was that the usual length of time it takes or not? (RECORD IN TABLE BELOW)

28. (IF "NOT USUAL TIME" FOR ANY ITEM) What is your usual time? (RECORD IN TABLE BELOW)

ASK EACH LINE GOING ACROSS IN THIS TABLE

ITEMS :	Q.25 How often done – Be sure enter unit (2x wk. or 3x mo., etc.)	Q.26 How long took last time in minutes	Q.27 Usual Time?		Q.28 If not usual time, enter usual time in minutes
			Yes	No	
Wash most windows outside					
Wash most windows inside					
Dust sills outside					
Dust sills inside					
Sweep sidewalk					
Wash sidewalk					
Wash or clean front door (not storm door)					
Vacuum living room rug					
Dust living room furniture					
Dust living room woodwork					
Thoroughly clean oven					

Notes to help understand above, if needed:

29. (HAND R. CARD A) Which <u>one</u> statement on this card best describes your own attitude towards your home?

1:	Cleanliness is one of the most important things. Most everything else should be sacrificed in order to have a clean, neat house. A woman should always think of cleaning first.	1
2:	Cleanliness is pretty important, but it doesn't really matter if some one thing gets dirty occasionally. A woman needs to be practical.	2
3:	Cleanliness <u>has</u> to take second place to <u>some</u> things. You shouldn't give <u>all</u> your time to it. A woman needs some outside interests.	3
4:	Cleanliness is not so important at all. Many other things are more important. A woman should spend her time on things that really matter.	4

30. Please tell me whether you feel each of these statements I'm going to read is true or false.

	TRUE	FALSE
a. A really good housekeeper always has her curtains clean.	1	2
b. You have to get up early to keep a house properly clean.	1	2
c. Dust is one of the worst problems in keeping a house clean.	1	2
d. With a family, a lot of clutter is something you can't help.	1	2
e. Doing dishes once a day is sensible.	1	2
f. You should have a schedule for cleaning to get it done right.	1	2
g. A woman is lazy who doesn't shake out small rugs every day.	1	2
h. White things, like sheets, towels and shirts, should be pure white always no matter how much trouble it takes.	1	2

189

31. Getting back to facts, I'd like to ask you about a few cleaning products you use. I'll ask you for the brand you most often buy, the size box, the cost as you recall it, and about how often you buy.

	Brand	Box Sizes (Lg., Med., Sm.)	Cost Per Box	How Often Purchase
Laundry detergent				
Scouring powder				
Liquid all-purpose cleaner				
Floor wax				
Window cleaner				
Oven cleaner				

32. Speaking of ovens, about how often do you use your oven in an ordinary week?

_____ times per week

33. Do you have a cleaning woman (or man) come into your house to help with the cleaning?

	Yes	1
(NEXT PAGE) SKIP TO Q.34c	No	2

34a. For how many hours in an ordinary week, do you have a cleaning woman (or man)?

_____ hrs. per week

34b. How much do you pay (her)(him) in a week?

$_____

35. Dogs and cats--pets--have something to do with cleaning. Do you have any dogs? Cats? - which are permitted in the house regularly?

		Yes	No
IF YES, ENTER NUMBER	Dogs		
	Cats		

36. Smoking has something to do with cleaning, too. Do any members of your household smoke?

	Yes	1
SKIP TO Q.39	No	2

37. How many people smoke?

ENTER # _____

38. What do they smoke? (FOR EACH) How many are smoked in a day in this house?

ENTER #

Cigarettes	
Cigars	
Pipes	

190

34c. If you could find someone to do your regular cleaning just like you do, would you be willing to hire someone for, say, 75¢ an hour?

	Yes	1
SKIP TO Q.34e	No	2

34d. (IF "YES" TO Q.34c) Would you be willing to hire someone for 90¢ an hour? $1.05? $1.20? $1.35? $1.50?

	YES	NO
90¢/hr.	1	2
$1.05/hr.	1	2
$1.20/hr.	1	2
$1.35/hr.	1	2
$1.50/hr.	1	2

ASK ONLY UNTIL
A "NO" ANSWER
IS OBTAINED

(CONTINUE WITH Q.35, FORMER PAGE)

34e. (IF "NO" TO Q.34c) Would you be willing to hire someone for 60¢ an hour? 45¢? 30¢? 15¢?

	YES	NO
60¢/hr.	1	2
45¢/hr.	1	2
30¢/hr.	1	2
15¢/hr.	1	2

ASK ONLY UNTIL
A "YES" ANSWER
IS OBTAINED

(CONTINUE WITH Q.35, FORMER PAGE)

Section III - Clothing and Clothing Maintenance

39. Turning now to clothing, tell me how long each of the following kinds of garments can be worn, in your opinion, before they need to be washed or drycleaned. If I mention a garment that isn't worn around your house, just say so. (RECORD IN TABLE BELOW)

40. (ASK AFTER ALL GARMENTS IN Q.39 ARE COVERED) Among these men's items (READ THEM AGAIN) what does your husband wear at work? (RECORD BELOW)

| GARMENTS | Q. 39 | | Q.40 |
	Time Can Be Worn Before Washing/Cleaning	Do Not Have or Wear	Husband Wears at Work
Men's			
Slacks			
White dress shirts			
Colored sports shirts			
Flannel or denim work shirts			
Dungarees or overalls			
Business suits (dress)			
Uniforms or company outfits			
Women's			
Slacks			
Cotton blouses, skirts, dresses			
Sweaters			
Better dresses			
Children's (1 year to 18 years)*			
Boys' cotton shirts			
Boys' pants or dungarees			
Girls' cotton blouses, skirts, dresses			
Girls' better dresses			

* CHECK HERE IF NO CHILDREN ONE TO 18 YEARS _____ AND OMIT REMAINDER OF QUESTION

41. How do you do the greatest part of your washing:

SKIP TO Q.43	In own washer	1
	At laundromat	2
	Send to laundry	3

42. In an average week, what does it cost to (do your laundry at a laundromat)(send it out to a laundry) - (WHICHEVER APPLICABLE)?

Cost per week _____

43. At this time of year, how do you dry the greatest part of your washing:

SKIP TO Q.45	In own dryer	1
	Outside on line	2
	Inside on line	3
	In laundromat dryer	4

44. Could it be that you own a dryer even though you aren't using it much this time of year?

| | Yes | 1 |
| | No | 2 |

45. In an average month this time of year what does it cost you to send things to be drycleaned?

Cost per month _____

Never use drycleaning _____

46. While we're talking about washing let's talk about washing cars. (CHECK HERE IF NO CARS _____ and skip to Q.49) How is your car most often washed (NEWEST CAR IF MORE THAN ONE)?

By a member of family	1
By somebody hired to do it	2
At a car wash	3
Other (SPECIFY)	4
It's never washed	5

47. About how often is this car washed? FREQUENCY:

48. When at home, is this car:

Always parked on street	1
Always parked in garage	2
Sometimes one, sometimes other.	3

193

Section IV - Expenditure of Tax Dollar

49. (HAND R. CARD B) This card lists services provided by the city which are paid for by your taxes. Suppose you could change the way the tax dollar is distributed. If you increase tax support for one or more services, and do not decrease others, the taxes will go up. Would you like to see <u>more</u> tax money spent on one or more of these services?

	Yes	1
SKIP TO Q. 52	No	2

50. On which services?

Police Protection	1
Fire Protection	2
Education	3
Air Pollution Control	4
Garbage and Trash Collection	5
Street & Highway Maintenance	6
Public Health & Hospital Services	7
Relief and Welfare Services	8
Cultural and Recreational Facilities	9

51. Which would you be willing to spend less on?

Police Protection	1
Fire Protection	2
Education	3
Air Pollution Control	4
Garbage and Trash Collection	5
Street and Highway Maintenance	6
Public Health and Hospital Services	7
Relief and Welfare Services	8
Cultural & Recreational Facilities	9
None	0

52. Suppose the Federal Government gave the city an additional 10¢ for every dollar of taxes the city collected. (REFER TO CARD B) How would you recommend that this additional money be spent?

Service	Amount to be Added
Police Protection	
Fire Protection	
Education	
Air Pollution Control	
Garbage and Trash Collection	
Street and Highway Maintenance	
Public Health & Hospital Services	
Relief and Welfare Services	
Cultural & Recreational Facilities	

Section V - Attitudes Toward Air Pollution

IF R. HAS MENTIONED AIR POLLUTION (DIRT, SOOT, ETC.), ANYWHERE IN THE
INTERVIEW, ASK Q.53. IF NOT, SKIP TO Q.54.

53. You have mentioned certain problems relating to air pollution (dirt, soot, etc. -
USE R's WORDS). Please describe to me in greater detail the problems you have
with--let's call it--air pollution.

54. Which of these things have you ever done:	Yes	No
a. Heard family or friends talking about the dirty or sooty air in this neighborhood?	1	2
b. Engaged in conversations yourself about the dirty or sooty air in this neighborhood?	1	2
c. Read any articles in newspapers and/or magazines about air pollution or dirty or sooty air?	1	2

55. (ASK ONLY IF "YES" TO Q.54c)
In which newspapers or
magazines?

Inquirer	1
Bulletin	2
Other (SPECIFY)	3

56. (HAND R. CARD C) In an overall way,
how would you rate the air in this
neighborhood? Just select the statement on the card which best describes
your opinion of the air in this neighborhood.

Air is extremely dirty - perhaps dirtiest in the city.	1
Air is quite dirty - perhaps dirtier than most other neighborhoods in the city.	2
Air is somewhat dirty - but no dirtier than other city neighborhoods.	3
Air is somewhat clean - but no cleaner than other city neighborhoods.	4
Air is quite clean - perhaps cleaner than most other neighborhoods in the city.	5
Air is extremely clean - perhaps cleanest in the city.	6

IF R. ANSWERED CODES 1, 2, 3 OR 4 IN
Q.56, CONTINUE WITH Q.57.

IF R. ANSWERED CODES 5 OR 6 IN Q.56,
SKIP TO SECTION VI DEMOGRAPHIC DATA

57a. Could you describe the air in this neighborhood further to me. Tell me what it is like.

57b. Compared with the air in your neighborhood, do you think any other area or areas in the city have greater air pollution problems?

Yes	1
No	2

58. Has this air pollution made for any specific health problems for you, your family, or anyone you know? (IF YES) What?

59. (IF ANY HEALTH PROBLEMS FOR SELF OR FAMILY IN Q.58) Have these health problems caused any special cleaning to be required? (IF YES) What kind?

60. How strongly do you feel about eliminating the air pollution problem? What thoughts do you have about that?

			Yes	1
61. Have you personally or cooperatively with others in your neighborhood ever done anything in an attempt to eliminate or relieve the air pollution problem?

		SKIP TO Q.63	Yes	1
			No	2

62. What was done?

63. Let's suppose the air pollution problem we've been discussing could be solved completely. How much would it be worth to you? (RECORD IN TABLE ON NEXT PAGE)

64. When you answered, what kind of a solution did you have in mind? (PROBE: Joint action of neighbors, device for own home only, service by city, etc.)

65. Suppose a device was invented which would take all of the dirt and soot out of the air around your house and inside it. It would eliminate any problem of air pollution for your house. How much would you be willing to pay for such a device? (RECORD IN TABLE ON NEXT PAGE)

66. Now suppose such a device were not possible but the problem could be solved by banding together with your neighbors. If you knew that everyone else was paying the same, how much would you be willing to pay to keep the neighborhood and your home clean--free of soot and air pollution? (RECORD IN TABLE ON NEXT PAGE)

RECORDING TABLE FOR Qs. 63, 65, 66. IN EACH CASE, READ AMOUNTS DOWN
UNTIL R. REJECTS AN AMOUNT AS TOO MUCH. CHECK OPPOSITE THAT AMOUNT.
CHECK LAST CATEGORY IF R. IS UNWILLING TO PAY ANYTHING.

AMOUNTS:	Q.63 Complete solution to air pollution problem.	Q.65 Device for around house and inside it.	Q.66 Neighbors together solving air pollution problems.
25¢ a month	1	1	1
50¢ a month	2	2	2
75¢ a month	3	3	3
$1.00 a month	4	4	4
$1.25 a month	5	5	5
$1.50 a month	6	6	6
$1.75 a month	7	7	7
$2.00 a month	8	8	8
More than $2.00 a month	9	9	9
No amount, nothing	0	0	0

Section VI - Demographic Data

67. HH Members (Rel. to Head)	68. Age	69. Last Grade of School Completed	70. Employed?			71. (CARD D) Approximate Annual Income for those Employed	72. Ethnic Origin
			Full Time	Part Time	No		
1. Male head							
2. Female head							
3.							* * * * * * * *
4.							* * * * * * * *
5.							* * * * * * * *
6.							* * * * * * * *
7.							* * * * * * * *
8.							* * * * * * * *
9.							* * * * * * * *
10.							* * * * * * * *

73. Precise description of male head of household's occupation:

74. (IF FEMALE HEAD EMPLOYED) Description of female head's occupation:

75. Does any member of the household have any current health problem? IF SO, LIST MEMBER # FROM ABOVE TABLE AND DESCRIBE HEALTH PROBLEM.

76. Do you own or rent this house?

SKIP TO Q.78	Own	1
	Rent	2

77. What is the amount of monthly rent you pay?

$ _____ per mo.

TERMINATE INTERVIEW

78. What would you estimate the market value of this home to be today? (If you were to sell your house today, what do you think you could get for it?)

$_____

APPENDIX E

SAMPLE OF QUESTIONNAIRES USED IN CHAPTER 5

Date_____

Address_____

Is soot and ash noticeable: Heavy_____
                              Average_____
                              Light_____
                              None_____

Side of street house located on: East____   West____

                                  North___   South____

Location of house: Corner House_____   Mid-Street_____

Hello. I'm a member of a survey research corporation.
We are interested in determining whether your cleaning
and maintenance procedures have been affected by the
soot and ash fallout episode of Friday evening, March 26th.
I'd like to ask you several questions.

1. Do you own or rent this residence?_____

2. How many people are there in your household?_____

    Is the person head of household, wife, or other?_____

    _____

    Estimated age of respondent(s)_____

Proceed to next page.

	Clean Sidewalks	Clean Driveways	Clean Porches and External Entrance Ways	Clean Outside Windows
Frequency				
Last Time				
If Recently, Time Before This				
Next Time				
Was Activity Affected How: Add'l Time Dirtier				
Was Cleaning Activity Normally Planned				
Reason for unusual Cleaning Activity				
Episode Hadn't Occurred, When Next Cleaning				
Per Cent Due to Air Pollution				
Cleaned by You or Family Member				
Time Spent				
Wage You Would be Willing to Pay Someone Else to Perform Task				
Was Task Performed by Someone Else. Yes-No				
Time Spent by Hired Help				
Hourly Wage				
Materials Used				
Cost				
Per Cent Used				

Dust Interior House	Clean Inside of Windows	Clean Drapes and Curtains	Clean Venetian Blinds	Shampoo Rug	Wash Woodwork

Clean Exterior Walls and Trim	Paint Exterior Walls and Trim	Clean Auto Garage, no Garage	Sweep and Vacuum Interior House	Mop and Wax Linoleum Floors

1. Were you affected in any other way than those we've just talked about?
    If so, in what way? (Record response)

_____

_____

_____

_____

_____

_____

What seemed to be person's attitude: Very annoyed_____

Moderately annoyed_____

Slightly annoyed_____

Not annoyed_____

We've talked about various ways in which you reacted to the fallout of soot
and ash in the neighborhood.

2. What would you have been willing to pay to have kept this incident from

    affecting you?_____

    (Had I been here that Friday evening before the soot and ash episode
    and told you what was about to happen, what would you have paid me
    to have kept your property from being affected?)

3. What is the market value of your residence?_____

4. How much rent do you pay per month?_____

If you have time, I have one more question I would like to ask you. This
question is unrelated to the previous material we've been discussing.

Listed below are a number of different public services financed by the taxes you pay to the city and state. We would like you to indicate whether you are satisfied or dissatisfied with the level and quality of services provided. You can do this in two ways.

(A) First, suppose you were given the chance to decide how much of your tax dollar should be spent on each service. Assuming that taxes do not change (do not increase), on which services would you like more spent, and on which less? (Record "more" as + and "less" as -). How much more or less out of each dollar? (Make the answer add to 0¢.)

(B) Now, suppose the government has taken your advice and changed the amounts it spends in the ways you indicate. Let us now give them more money to spend. For every $1.00 they had before, they now have $1.10. How would you like to see this added 10¢ spent?

PUBLIC SERVICE	QUESTION A	QUESTION B
Education	_____	_____
Fire Protection	_____	_____
Police Protection	_____	_____
Refuse Collection and Disposal	_____	_____
Air Pollution Control	_____	_____
Streets and Highways	_____	_____
Public Health and Hospitals	_____	_____
Relief and Welfare Expenditures	_____	_____
Cultural and Recreational Facilities	_____	_____
Total	0¢	10¢

APPENDIX F
DESCRIPTION AND SOURCES OF DATA
FOR CHAPTER 6

The following list describes the variables used in this study and indicates sources or methods of measurement. All data are by census tracts of the St. Louis SMSA, and unless otherwise specified are for the year 1960.

A. Dependent Variable

MPV - Median value of owner-occupied single-family housing units, estimated by owner as of April, 1960. From U.S. Bureau of the Census, U.S. Censuses of Population and Housing: 1960, St. Louis, Mo.-Ill., Final Report PCH (1)-131, U.S. Government Printing Office, Washington, D.C., 1962, Table H-2. (Henceforth this publication is referred to by its final report number.)

B. Independent Variables Used in Final Equations

SUL - An index of annual geometric mean sulfation levels for the period February 20, 1963, to February 10, 1964. An index number running from 1 through 8 was assigned to each census tract, a value of one representing levels equal to or less than 0.49 mg. of $SO_3/100cm^2/day$, a value of two for sulfation levels of 0.50 to 0.74 on the same scale, and so on up to a value of eight for those tracts having pollution levels equal to or greater than 2.0 mg. $SO_3/100 \ cm^2/day$.

The figures were interpolated from an isopleth map developed from 41 stations by the Interstate Air Pollution Study. Measurements are made by measuring the amount of SO_3 formed on the surface

of a cylinder coated with lead dioxide and exposed
for one month. See Jack R. Farmer, Interstate
Air Pollution Study, Air Quality Measurements
(Interstate Air Pollution Study, St. Louis-East St.
Louis Metropolitan Area, February, 1965, p. 6;
Figure 75, p. 144.

MNR - median number of rooms per housing unit, from
       PHC (1)-131, Table H-1.

PRB - percentage recently built. Housing units built from
       1950 to March, 1960, as percentage of all housing
       units, from PHC (1)-131, Table H-1.

HPM - total houses per square mile (in thousands).
       Total housing units from PHC (1)-131, Table H-1;
       total area of tracts in square miles calculated from
       maps obtained from School of Architecture, Wash-
       ington University, St. Louis.

TIZ - time zone. The metropolitan area was divided into
       zones representing average time during rush hour
       (7:30 a.m., 1960) required for an express bus to
       reach the central business district, according to
       records provided by the St. Louis Metropolitan
       Transit Authority. Each census tract was assigned
       a number depending upon the zone within which it fell.

Zone	Minutes to CBD
1	0-10
2	11-20
3	21-30
4	31-40
5	more than 40

PNW - percentage nonwhite housing units. Nonwhite
       owner- and renter-occupied units as a percentage
       of all occupied units.

SCH - school quality. The presence of SCH1 and SCH2
       in an equation indicated the use of a three-fold

ranking of census tracts according to the value its
school district has in terms of selling a house.
SCH1 is a one/zero dummy variable for above-
average quality; and SCH2 is a similar variable for
average quality. If only SCH1 appears in an equation,
a two-fold classification of school quality has been
used (above average, 1; otherwise, 0). The judgments on school quality were based on interviews
with educators who were asked how they believed
that people in general evaluated the schools in 1960
and with real-estate salesmen who were asked how
advantageous different school districts were in selling a house in 1960. Close agreement among the
interviewees was found.

OCR - occupation ratio. Ratio of number of craftsmen,
foremen, operatives and laborers to total number of
employed persons, from David J. Pittman and Sarah
L. Boggs, "An Analysis of Population, Housing,
Crime and Delinquency Characteristics in the St.
Louis Study Area," Mimeo., 1963.

HWA - highway accessibility. One if census tract touched
a highway or major thoroughfare, zero otherwise.
The thoroughfares included were the Daniel Boone
Expressway, Chippewa-Route 66, Gravois, Lindbergh,
Kingshighway, Broadway-Lemay Ferry-Bellfontain
Rd., Big Bend, River Des Peres-McCausland-
Skinker-Hodiamont, Mark Twain Expressway, and
Riverview-Route 67 North.

ILL - Illinois/Missouri dummy variable: one/zero for in
Illinois/Missouri.

PPU - persons per unit; population divided by all occupied
units, from PHC (1)-131, Tables P-1 and H-2.

MFI - median family income, 1959, from PHC (1)-131,
Table P-1.

C. Independent Variables Used in Preliminary Equations Only.

HIV - index of annual geometric mean concentrations of
suspended particulates gathered by high-volume air
samplers for the period July 1, 1963, to July 1, 1964.
The index numbers run from 0 to 10, each higher
number representing an increase of $10mg/m^3$ with
an index of zero for $60mg/m^3$ or less and 10 for
greater than 150 mg/m^3. The figures for census
tracts were interpolated from an isopleth map developed from 17 stations by the Interstate Air
Pollution Study. See Jack R. Farmer, op.cit.,
Figure 11.

PSS - percentage substandard. Percentage of all units
dilapidated or lacking other plumbing facilities,
from PHC (1)-131, Table H-1.

CRM - crime rate; the number of criminal offenses (criminal homocide, rape, robbery, aggravated assault,
burglary, larceny and auto theft) per 10,000, rounded
to hundreds. Information was gathered from individual police districts and applied to census tracts.

SAA - shopping area accessibility. One/zero for include/
exclude a major regional shopping district, based
on U.S. Department of Commerce reports and personal knowledge of the area. Eleven regional centers
were chosen for this designation.

IAA - industrial area accessibility. One/zero for include/
exclude an industrial area, based on areas shown on
U.S. Geological Survey Maps.

Social Area Analysis Indexes
Because of their availability the social rank, urbani-
zation and segregation indexes contained in the Pittman and Boggs study, op.cit., were tried in one run.
Since they did not work as well as the above variables, some of which are included in these indexes,

and since the rationale for them is questionable, they
were dropped after a preliminary trial.

APPENDIX G
CONSTRUCTION OF PROPERTY VALUE INDEXES
USED IN CHAPTER 7

The same basic data were used for the construction of the regression and median indexes. The data consisted of estimates of market sale prices based on tax stamps of properties in both the affected and control areas over the years 1957 to the first half of 1964. Any property that was sold at least once during the period provided data for our sample. For each of these properties, regardless of when it was sold during the 1957-64 period, the 1957 assessed value was also obtained.

The first step in the data preparation was to estimate 1957 property values from the 1957 assessed values. All 1957 assessed values were multiplied by the factor 3.563. This figure is the geometric mean of the ratios of 1957 sale value to 1957 assessed values based on all properties that were sold in 1957. After this adjustment was made, 1957 assessed values were replaced by 1957 sale values where these were available. Thus every piece of property in the sample was in effect assigned a 1957 sale value -- either an inflated 1957 assessed value or a 1957 sale value.

The basic data for the median index were then obtained by taking the ratio of each sale price to the 1957 value for the same piece of property. Thus, the median value for the year 1959 was obtained as the median of all such ratios where there was a sale in 1959. Obviously, the ratio where the sale occurred in 1957 was always unity.

The regression index was calculated in the following way, after a method developed by Bailey, Muth, and Nourse.[5] The

---

[1]M. J. Bailey, R. F. Muth, and H. O. Nourse, "A Regression

dependent variable in this regression analysis is the log of the
current sale value to the previous sale value. Where there
was only one sale on a given piece of property over the entire
period 1957-64, this ratio would, of course, be the same as the
ratio used in the construction of the median index discussed
above. The independent variables in this regression are a set
of dummy variables, one for each of the years 1958-64. The
dummy variables are such that any given variable will
(1) assume the value +1 if the year in which the final sale
occurs is the year to which the dummy variable refers;
(2) assume the value -1 if the earlier sale occurs in the year to
which the dummy refers; and (3) assume the value zero otherwise. The antilog of each regression coefficient is the estimated index value for the year to which the dummy variable
refers.

"Method for Real Estate Price Index Construction, " Journal of
the American Statistical Association, No. 304, Vol. 58 (Dec., 196
pp. 933-42.

ABOUT THE AUTHOR

Ronald G. Ridker, Associate Professor of Economics at the Maxwell School, Syracuse University, is currently on leave from the university. He is a member of the Policy Planning Division of the Agency for International Development in Washington, D. C. He has been on the staff of Washington University and the Brookings Institution and has served as a consultant to UNESCO in Thailand and to the Hudson Institute.

This book is the outgrowth of a three-year study for the U. S. Public Health Service on the economic problems of air pollution. Dr. Ridker is also the author of professional articles in other fields of economics.

Dr. Ridker received his Ph. D. from the University of Wisconsin in 1958. He is a graduate of the University of California at Berkeley and the Fletcher School of Law and Diplomacy. He was granted a Fulbright Fellowship for additional study and research at the University of Oslo, Norway.